# RELIGIOUS FAITH MEETS MODERN SCIENCE

Sgt Walter Michura
4 Furnace Road
Chester, NJ 07930-2120

★ Once a Marine, ★
Always a Marine

Paulinus F. Forsthoefel, S.J., M. Sc., S.T.L., Ph.D.
Professor Emeritus of Biology
University of Detroit
Fellow of the American Association for the Advancement of Science
Fellow of The Ohio Academy of Science


Member of:

Sigma Xi: The Scientific Research Society of America
Genetics Society of America
American Genetic Association
Michigan Academy of Science, Arts, and Letters

# Religious Faith
# Meets Modern Science

Paulinus F. Forsthoefel, SJ, MSc, STL, PhD

ALBA·HOUSE    NEW·YORK

SOCIETY OF ST. PAUL, 2187 VICTORY BLVD., STATEN ISLAND, NEW YORK 10314

Library of Congress Cataloging-in-Publication Data

Forsthoefel, Paulinus F.
    Religious faith meets modern science / Paulinus F. Forsthoefel.
        p.      cm.
    Includes bibliographical references.
    ISBN 0-8189-0704-5
    1. Religion and science. I. Title.
BL240.2.F65      1994
261.5'5 — dc20                                      94-14611
                                                    CIP

---

Produced and designed in the United States of America by the
Fathers and Brothers of the Society of St. Paul,
2187 Victory Boulevard, Staten Island, New York 10314,
as part of their communications apostolate.


ISBN: 0-8189-0704-5

---

---

**Printing Information:**

---

Current Printing - first digit     1    2    3    4    5    6    7    8    9    10

---

Year of Current Printing - first year shown

1994          1995          1996          1997          1998          1999

---

# Contents

# Introduction

My interest in nature goes back to my earliest years in rural Ohio, when as a toddler my older brothers and sisters gave me a fledgling bluebird as a pet. Unfortunately, the pet did not survive long because I could not feed it properly, so I conducted a funeral service for it under the apple trees of our orchard. Was this an intimation of my lifelong twin interests: science and religion? In high school I became fascinated by birds. I raised pigeons and bought a goose at the local poultry market. The goose survived only a few months, but long enough to provide the main dish for a dinner hosted by my father, the county auditor, for his deputies. All I got for my share of the goose was the neck. During my last three years in high school I joined the Indiana Audubon Society and the Wilson Ornithological Club and participated in their meetings. I spent much time in the woods and fields around my town of Celina, Ohio, with a binocular studying the birds as they came and went in their migrations. All these efforts were not wasted; eventually they were included in a monograph on the birds of the area.

All my life I had the example of what deep religious faith meant to my parents. So it was not surprising that when time came in my last year of high school to choose a profession, I chose the priesthood in the Society of Jesus (the Jesuits). After two years of novitiate at Milford, Ohio, I pronounced my religious vows. Then came two years of studying English, Latin,

Greek, history, and public speaking. At the end of these two years, I was asked by Allen Farrell, in charge of graduate studies, what field I would like to follow. Since I had become greatly interested in Greek literature and was getting my A.B. in it, I said "Greek literature." Unexpectedly Farrell said: "Everybody says you should study biology." During my first four years as a Jesuit I had kept up my interest in bird study and probably that is why Farrell made his remark.

Anyhow now I am glad that I did not go further in Greek studies. I began formal college study of biology at the University of Detroit during several summers when free from the regular sequence of my training as a Jesuit. That sequence involved three years of philosophy and four years of theology at West Baden College, Indiana. The three years of philosophy and the four years of theology were separated by three years of high school teaching of mathematics. Ordination to the priesthood came after three years of theology and the degree of Licentiate of Theology (qualifying me to teach theology) after four years of theology. I was fortunate that West Baden College was located in the unglaciated hill country of southern Indiana, a region rich in all kinds of plants and animals and also in fossils exposed in limestone and sandstone outcroppings. Where else could one find ten species of oak, timber rattlesnakes, blind cave fish, and rare sea-lily fossils, all not far from the back door (the "taxi entrance") of the college? I spent much of my free time collecting the plants, animals, and fossils from the hills and valleys around the college.

After a final year of Jesuit training (the "tertianship") at Parma, Ohio, I began at Ohio State University four years of study and research in genetics. My advisor, Earl L. Green, was a "mouse geneticist," so I took as my doctoral research project the embryological development of a gene mutation in the mouse affecting the skeleton. After receiving the Ph.D. degree, I left Columbus, Ohio, for Detroit, Michigan, to join the faculty of the biological department of the University of Detroit. Here I taught under-graduate and graduate courses in genetics and carried on an extensive research program on several skeletal mutations in the mouse. Research is expensive and mine was supported by grants from the National Science Foundation and the National Institutes of Health. The results of my research I reported at meetings of the Genetics Society of America and in numerous journals (*Genetics, Journal of Heredity, Journal of Anatomy, Journal of Morphology*, etc.). Besides state and national meetings I participated in three International Congresses of Genetics (at Montreal, Canada; Berkeley, California; The Hague, Netherlands).

In all public appearances as a scientist, I made no effort to disguise the fact that I am also a committed man of faith. I always wore clerical garb (the Roman collar) at the scientific meetings I attended. I was aware that some of my colleagues thought it remarkable that I could be a bona fide scientist and a priest at the same time. I also knew that often young men and women coming with naive and unexamined religious beliefs to secular universities such as Ohio State could not justify their religious beliefs when challenged by scientific theories and therefore abandoned their religious practices. I myself had to face the same challenges and come to some honest resolution of them.

The present work then is a series of essays which contain my reflections on natural science, religious faith, and their interactions including possible conflicts. The material given is based on the work of many authors. I give references to the most important works consulted in the lists of suggested readings after each chapter. I caution the reader that the readings suggested are given because they provide background for the discussions in each chapter, and not because I necessarily agree with all the views expressed in them. I wrote the work not as a formal scientific treatise comprehensible only by experts in the fields. Rather I tried to write in the style one finds in the articles of science in the magazines *Time* or *Newsweek* and understandable with a little effort by any educated person. The Glossary at the end of the work should help readers unfamiliar with the meaning of some terms. I sincerely hope that my work will help religious believers, Catholic or non-Catholic, to reconcile their religious beliefs with scientific facts.

A number of people have read the manuscript of the work and have encouraged me to have it published. I particularly thank Gerry Albright, Fred Henley, John Staudenmaier, and Jim Williams for suggesting many clarifications and improvements.

## SUGGESTED READINGS

1. Barbour, Ian G., *Issues in Science and Religion* (New York, NY: Harper and Row, 1966).

2. Barbour, Ian G., *Science and Religion*. Harper Forum Books, Martin E. Marty, Gen. ed. (New York, NY: Harper and Row, 1968).

3. McMullin, Ernan, "Introduction: Evolution and Creation," pp. 1-56 in *Evolution and Creation*, Ernan McMullin, ed. (Notre Dame, IN: University of Notre Dame Press, 1985).

4. Polkinghorne, John, *One World: The Interaction of Science and Theology* (Princeton, NJ: Princeton University Press, 1987).

5. Rahner, Karl, "Science and Christian Faith," pp. 3-162 in *Theological Investigations*, vol. XXI, trans. Hugh M. Riley (New York, NY: Crossroad, 1988).

6. Russell, Robert J., William R. Stoeger, and George V. Coyne, editors, *Physics, Philosophy, and Theology: A*

*Common Quest for Understanding* (Notre Dame, IN: University of Notre Dame Press, 1988).

7. Wright, Robert, "Science, God, and Man," pp. 38-44 in *Time*, v. 140, December 28, 1992.

# RELIGIOUS FAITH MEETS MODERN SCIENCE

# CHAPTER 1

# What Do Scientists Do?

The world is full of interesting natural phenomena. Many people have been fascinated by the behavior of ants. Some ants are slave-makers, some use their larvae as sewing machines to fasten leaves together for nests, some have members serving as storage barrels for plant juices, some act like farmers using aphids as their "cows," etc. Some scientists spend their entire lives collecting and cataloging natural phenomena. Necessary as this preliminary work is, more important is the effort to understand what is back of these phenomena.

So scientists are thrilled when they find out the basis of some natural phenomenon. A classic example is Archimedes. He is said to have leaped out of his bath-tub and to have run naked down the streets of Syracuse (Sicily), shouting "Eureka" ("I have found it!") when the idea came to him how to test the gold crown of the king for fraudulent admixture of silver. When he immersed himself in the bath-tub, the water overflowed, displaced by his body. Archimedes realized that silver mixed with the gold of a crown of a given weight would increase its bulk and so cause the crown to displace more water that one of pure gold.

An assumption behind all science work is that there is a constancy in the workings of nature: given such and such conditions present and such and such agents operating, certain phenomena will follow. The natural scientist may express such regular sequences of events as natural "laws." Thus an idealized sequence is: first, observations of certain phenomena; second, an hypothesis on the relationship between these phenomena; third, testing of the hypothesis with emphasis on its power of prediction of new phenomena; fourth, the expression of a confirmed hypothesis (theory) as a "law." The hypothesis advanced must be "falsifiable," i.e., must be capable of being disproved, to be a scientific hypothesis. The scientist is never confident that he or she has discovered absolute truth. Further observations may make what appeared to be a well-founded hypothesis (theory) or even "law" to be untenable, or at least in need of modification. One objection raised to this representation of the "scientific method" is that it unrealistically separates observations (collection of data) from theory. The objectors maintain that no scientist can collect data without some theory biasing what he or she thinks is a relevant observation. Thus complete objectivity in a scientific investigation is an illusion. If the alleged scientific method is a myth, then how do scientists work? The following concrete example may be enlightening.

Alzheimer's disease is a well-known condition afflicting many millions of people as they age. The affected people gradually lose their mental functions and regress to a stage where they may not even know who they are. Examination of the brains of these people has revealed that the brains contain tangles of fibrils not found in normal brains. Study of these fibrils by Glenner and Wong of the University of California, San Diego, found that they contain an abnormal protein called beta-amyloid. The question arises: Is beta-amyloid the cause of the degeneration of the affected nerve cells or rather the effect, a product of the degeneration which is due to some other basic defect in the nerve cells? If the cause, a treatment preventing the formation of the beta-amyloid could possibly reverse the degeneration of the cells, a cure then for Alzheimer's disease. Many neuroscientists are seeking an answer to this puzzle. A group of researchers headed by Bruce Yankner at Harvard injected beta-amyloid in the brains of rats and found nerve cell degeneration similar to that observed in Alzheimer's patients. Injection of a brain protein called substance P protected the nerve cells from beta-amyloid's neurotoxic effects.

Were these results real? A number of neuroscientists immediately tried to reproduce Yankner's results. Some could reproduce them; others failed. Those who did observe neural degeneration also reported much variability in the results depending on such factors as the source of the beta-amyloid, the solvent used to dissolve it for injection, and whether it aggregated or not. Some investigators involved in the controversy over the reality of Yankner's results have connections with drug companies and presumably would like to develop their own animal models and drug for treatment of Alzheimer's disease. An effective drug could bring millions of dollars in sales to the company marketing it.

In this example of actual scientists at work we see a characteristic of much contemporary science: many scientists are attacking the same problem and each attempting to contribute something to its solution. Their motives are mixed: establishing the truth of the matter, establishing priority and recognition for themselves, securing possible financial profits. Eventually we can expect solid progress to a solution of the problem.

Scientists, whether working alone or as part of a group, form a community. They accept the "paradigm" of the community and offer their contributions on the basis of the paradigm adopted by the community at the time. One paradigm already referred to is that any explanation proposed for the phenomena he or she has observed must at least be theoretically subject to empirical falsification. So in biology any attempt to explain vital phenomena by hypothesizing a vital principle or "entelechy" will not be accepted because the hypothesis cannot be experimentally tested. A related paradigm in biology is that all vital phenomena should as far as possible be reduced to a molecular basis in physics and chemistry. This reductionist approach has been immensely successful in my field of genetics. Since the explanation of the chemical structure of the gene by Nobel prize winners Watson and Crick (1962) in terms of deoxyribonucleic acid (DNA) and the working out of the genetic code by Nirenberg, Holley, Matthaei, and Khorana (for which they received the Nobel prize in 1968) and their associates, a series of brilliant researches has explained how genes control heredity, how changes in heredity arise by alterations of the genes and chromosomes, and so forth.

Does the scientist make any use of "belief" or "reliance on authority" in his or her researches? Probably if asked, the scientist would indignantly deny it. Yet the scientist does *assume*, i.e., believes that natural phenomena always follow definite "laws" which involve only natural causality. Therefore his or her efforts to discover these laws are not fruitless or vain efforts. However the scientist by his or her methods cannot rigorously prove this assumption. Further the individual scientist may say he or she places no reliance on authority, i. e., the testimony to the existence of some fact or process given by another. Yet, practically speaking, the scientist must assume a great deal on the words of other scientists. It is clearly impossible now, if it were ever possible, to begin a scientific investigation by checking first all the work done and accepted by the community of scientists in the field. This statement is so obvious that it needs no proof.

In modern life the scientist has acquired immense prestige. This in part is due to the tremendous technical advances which the discoveries of scientists have made possible. Thus the discovery of materials with semiconductor properties led to the preparation of micro-chips and these in turn to the invention of computers. Computers made possible round-trips to the moon

4

and a host of applications in all aspects of modern life. Imagine the amazement and wonder of one of our ancestors brought back to life as he or she surveys all the tools provided for man's well-being by modern technology. Night is banished by electric lights, distant events are brought into the home by TV via satellites, food is preserved fresh in an electric refrigerator and quickly prepared in a microwave oven, travel to Paris for a shopping tour is made possible by supersonic jet, and so forth and so on.

It is no wonder that some scientists intoxicated by their successes in understanding and manipulating nature have thought that only science gives real knowledge and that scientific methods can be extended to all aspects of life. What cannot be explained "scientifically" has for them no reality but is mere wishful thinking or an illusion. It is important to realize that the extension of scientific methods to demand the exclusion of other avenues to knowledge is an assumption that cannot be validated on a scientific basis. The methods of science cannot prove or disprove the existence of entities outside of the natural phenomena accessible to them. So when scientists proclaim that only material things exist and deny the possibility of non-material entities (e.g., a human soul) existing, they are making unproved assertions. Faith is not in conflict with true science but it is in conflict with the dogmatic materialism of some scientists.

The December 28, 1992 issue of *Time* magazine contained a feature article "Science, God, and Man." Reading this article, I found it interesting, to say the least, that towards the end of the 20th century, some "big-name" scientists are admitting that they cannot answer "scientifically" the ultimate questions about the universe, such as why it seems designed for the emergence of intelligent life (man).

## SUGGESTED READINGS

1. Bauer, Henry H., *Scientific Literacy and the Myth of the Scientific Method*, Urbana, IL: University of Illinois Press, 1992.

2. Marx, Jean, "Alzheimer's Debate Boils Over," *Science*: 257: 1336-1338, 1992.

3. Savage, C. Wade, ed., *Scientific Theories*, Minnesota Studies in the Philosophy of Science, vol. 14, University of Minnesota Press, 1990.

4. Wright, Robert, "Science, God and Man," pp. 38-44 in *Time*, v. 140, December 28, 1992.

# CHAPTER 2

# Religious Myths and Religious Faith

A nthropologists now agree with almost complete unanimity that humans from the beginning of their presence on the earth have shown concern about the ultimate explanation for the existence of the world and their own role in it and their destiny. This concern is shown in the religious myths they have carefully preserved and handed down from generation to generation. In these myths they explain the origin of the universe and the origin of man as due to the operations of some superior beings. Often these were personifications of natural phenomena which appeared especially beyond human control, such as the storm or the sea. The multitude of these "gods" were often thought of as related by generation and could be arranged in a pantheon. An example of this is the work of Hesiod for the gods of the Greeks, e.g., "Ouranos begot Kronos; Kronos begot Zeus," and so forth. Often among the community of the gods one was assigned a leading role — an approach to monotheism. Thus Zeus was preeminent among the Greek gods. The activities of the gods were conceived according to the ways their devotees acted. Thus in the creation myth of the Babylonians, *Enuma elish*, the gods met in an assembly and deliberated what they should do to resist the machinations of one of their number.

After people had settled into villages and were dependent on their cultivated fields for food, they were impressed profoundly by the cycle of the growth of their food plants, as it in turn followed the cycle of the seasons. Thus crops ripened in the summer, were harvested in the fall, died down in the winter, and began growth again in the spring with the new sowing. So, to ensure good crops, these people in the spring appealed to the god of fertility (Baal for the Canaanites) and performed religious rites in his honor. The god was conceived as dying with the crops in the winter and rising to new life in the spring. Not surprisingly, the fertility rites took on a sexual expression involving sacred prostitution in the temple of the god of fertility. Using their natural reason, these peoples evolved and sometimes codified a system of laws governing their relations with each other in marriage, business, the law court, and so forth. A famous example is the Code of Hammurabi. These codes show a good feeling for what is right and just. But they have limitations, as for example in the frequent invoking of the death penalty for infractions. Man relying on his own reason and experiences developed a very limited religion, a mixture of good and bad practices and beliefs. Especially notable are the polytheistic aspects.

Christians, Jews, and Moslems believe that God intervened at a definite time in human history. Some time around 1800 B.C., God asked a man called Abram to leave the pagan environment of Haran, Mesopotamia, and to set out for a new land where he would worship and serve the one true God. Abram responded in faith to this call and, renamed Abraham, became the founder of a line of people who would practice the cult of the one true God. What is meant by religious faith is clearly shown by the response of Abraham. By religious faith we mean taking as true on the word of God what God reveals to us. This is precisely what Abraham did.

Religious faith is the response expected by God from man when man is made aware of God's revelation. Religious faith is not possible to humans' unaided powers and is a supernatural gift (grace) from God. For religious faith takes as true God's revelation solely on the basis of the authority of God revealing "who cannot deceive or be deceived." However, religious faith is not simple credulity. Religious faith requires that the would-be believer has certain evidence that God is truly revealing and requires assent to the truths revealed. The revealed truths that a Christian is asked to believe with this supernatural faith are summarized in statements such as the Apostles Creed and the Nicene Creed.

Most Christians, as other believers, are born and raised in their religious faith. They receive the gift of supernatural faith at their initiation into their religion, usually as infants when they are baptized. When they reach the age of "reason," they become free to accept this gift of faith or reject it. They may never be conscious of this ratification of their faith unless challenged by objections raised against it. This may happen in a class in biology at some university when the professor claims that the evidences for evolution have destroyed any role for a divine being in the creation of life. As mentioned in the Introduction, I intend the present work to reassure the troubled Christian believer by showing that his faith and the established findings of science are quite compatible and do not contradict each other.

Religious faith gives supernatural certitude about truths, some of which are accessible to natural reason with more or less clarity, and others of which are entirely beyond the grasp of natural reason. Thus man can have natural certitude that God exists, but natural reason can tell man nothing about the existence of a Trinity of Persons in the Unity of the Godhead. To obtain this information the help of supernatural faith is needed. From this example we see that when supernatural faith gives information, it does not always provide understanding. When understanding fails, we say that we know a "mystery."

God's revelations were not given all at once nor at once in

all clarity. God's revelation in the Old Testament emphasized the unicity of the Godhead against the errors of polytheistic cults. Only in God's revelation given in the New Testament do we find a clear revelation of the Trinity of Persons (Father, Son and Holy Spirit).

While the original revelations were made in some kind of theophany to individuals, eventually they were recorded in writing. Thus we have the origin of the Bible. The books of the Bible are very often compilations of several versions of the original revelation. The Scriptures, especially the Old Testament, show ample evidence of the editorial activities of redactors. In reading the Scriptures as the Word of God recording revelations, we must attend to their purpose. While often enough they record actual historical events (and in recent years their overall accuracy has been confirmed from various sources such as other historical documents, archaeological material, etc.), yet their primary purpose was to transmit the revelation of God's justice, mercy, and goodness to man. Sometimes they put into historical context material which has only a slight connection with actual historical events. I have in mind here particularly the story of Noah and the Deluge. This account is a myth, a narrative that describes and portrays in symbolic language the origin of the basic elements and assumptions of a culture, in this case of how God dealt with human wickedness without destroying the whole world and every creature in it, and ultimately entered into a new covenant with the survivors. It is not a detailed narrative of an historic event though there may have been in the collective memory of the people at the time it was recorded some basis in fact related to a devastating flood in the distant past. The editor, who combined at least two different stories, was reminding readers of God's special relationship with them which persisted despite man's sinfulness.

The writers of the Scriptures obviously were children of their times and shared with their contemporaries their inadequate knowledge of the world of nature. For instance, they conceived of the earth as a flat disk floating on a sea underneath (the origin of springs) and above the earth a "firmament" over which was yet another sea, the source of the rain. The sun was thought of as revolving around the earth, since it appeared to rise in the east, pass over the firmament above, and then descend in the west, to resume its circuit the next day. The writers of the Scriptures were not inspired to reveal truths of science, but truths about God and the Creator's designs for human beings. The guarantee of the truth of what is written in the Scriptures does not extend to scientific matters. It is a great mistake to look for scientific information in the Scriptures. We will examine this matter in more detail in later chapters.

Perhaps the greatest obstacle for religious belief met by a Christian believer in his or her own reflections and coming also from unbelievers, is the obvious existence of evil in the world. Evil seems to negate any possibility of a loving God and of a revelation from Him. I am not thinking here of moral evil (sin). Sin is perhaps inevitable considering the fact that man is free to obey or disobey God's commandments. Rather I am thinking of things like natural catastrophes (floods, earthquakes, fires, plagues) which apparently destroy indiscriminately the good and the bad alike. Plainly this is not a perfect world. If God is all-powerful and all-loving, why did God create a world in which there is so much suffering? One answer is that the Creator did not, but suffering came in as a retribution for the sin of the first man ("original sin") when he disobeyed God. While this answer still tries the faith of the Christian believer, it offers nothing to the unbeliever. For the unbeliever a more acceptable answer might be that God created a world good enough to serve as the theater of man's activities, yet imperfect enough to force man to use his own ingenuity and skills to control the forces of nature including the destructive ones. A third answer, satisfying again only to a Christian believer, is that all sufferings, all injustices and inequities, will be set right in the next life. In the final analysis, the problem of evil in the world remains unsolved.

Historically, religious authorities have been reluctant to revise their views to accommodate scientific advances. This is evident in the slow acceptance of evolution in place of special creation for the origin of life forms in the world. This reluctance is understandable since religious authorities feel a moral obligation to preserve a divinely revealed body of doctrine whose source is a God who cannot deceive, who is Truth itself and who is the origin of all truth. Therefore religious authorities require clear and certain evidence that what they thought as divinely revealed needs to be interpreted in a sense that is different from that accepted perhaps for many centuries. It is understandable too that scientists have been impatient with this conservatism of religious authorities and complain that they are hindering the progress of science. But that is beginning to change. At a recent symposium on science and Christian faith held in the spring of 1993 at Notre Dame University, many speakers mentioned the new climate which is emerging between science and faith, and how both science and faith have learned in recent decades not to identify knowledge with an over-confident certainty, stressing the key role which humility must play in both domains. Religious authorities increasingly acknowledge and praise the work of scientists and have shown a willingness to modify their views when the evidence presented is so strong that no rational person would deny it. Scientists, on the other hand, are admitting the fallacy of placing too much confidence in any one piece of evidence from science, because "the scientific truths of today all too easily prove to be the scientific errors of tomorrow."

SUGGESTED READINGS

1. Flannery, Austin, O.P., Gen. Ed., *Vatican Council II: The Conciliar and Post Conciliar Documents, Vol. I*, "Dogmatic Constitution on Divine Revelation" (Boston, MA: St. Paul Editions, 1988), pp. 750-765.

CHAPTER 3

---

# Does Science Contradict Faith?

C an what we accept on supernatural faith and the findings of science contradict each other? *A priori* one would say no. What is true for one should be true for the other. However, what if they *appear* to contradict each other? For example, the accounts of creation in Genesis state that God created all living things including human beings just as they are by simple "Fiat!" Yet natural science says that all its evidence supports the idea that a long process of evolution from non-life to life to man brought about the living world as we see it today. Apparent contradictions like this one force each side to reexamine just what their evidence supports. The evidence for evolution is constantly increasing. We will examine this evidence in a later chapter. There is no reason to think that natural scientists need abandon evolution as the explanation for the natural origin of living things. The resolution of this impasse has come from a more critical examination of just what God revealed in Genesis and in Scripture in general. Though God inspired the writers of Scripture to write down what God wanted, we now realize very clearly that the cultural experiences and ideas of the writers influenced *how* they communicated God's revelation.

In particular, the writers were not given any special knowledge about the natural world and therefore made use of the concepts that they had in common with their contemporaries. Moreover they knew nothing about a possible evolutionary origin of the world of life. They were inspired to write that the one God was the final origin of all things in the universe but they had no revelation about *how* the one God created. In other words, God's revelation to the Sacred Writers was concerned with man's ultimate concerns. Man's relation to God as the object of devotion and service is the chief concern, and not with how the world concretely came into existence. God was concerned to inform humans how they could attain their supernatural destiny. For this purpose it was sufficient that they know that all people and the universe came from God. A little common-sense reflection tells us that it would not have served any good purpose for God to reveal an evolutionary origin of living things at this pre-scientific stage of human culture. Besides the fact that humans lacked the extensive scientific background to understand and to validate the evolutionary hypothesis, the hypothesis was irrelevant to God's purposes and would only distract from them. If we bear in mind that God's revelation was never meant to provide the understanding of how the natural world operates by its natural forces, we will not find it contradicting what humans have discovered about this over the years to the present. Religious faith cannot contradict true science. It can and does contradict "scientism" which denies any role for a supernatural being in the world.

I said above that the inspired writers of Scripture necessarily followed the current ways of understanding natural phenomena in their writings. We must not take these culturally conditioned ways as part of the divine revelation made to them. The same observation can be made of their use of myths current at their time. A striking example is the story of the Deluge. The story as related in Genesis has striking similarities to the deluge story widely circulated and passed down from the remote past among the peoples of the Tigris-Euphrates area. Thus in the Gilgamesh epic, written around 2000 B.C., Utnapishtim (Noah) builds a square vessel and loads it with all species of animals. The flood rises until it covers the mountains; the vessel, as the water recedes, comes aground on a mountain and Utnapishtim sends out birds to reconnoiter the area (the dove and the swallow return, but the raven does not); and, finally, after emerging from the vessel, Utnapishtim offers a sacrifice to his god.

Scripture scholars agree that the writer of Genesis (ca. 650 B.C.) appropriated the outlines of this story from his pagan neighbors, placed it in a different setting purged of its polytheistic elements, and used it to introduce a covenant between the one true God and living creatures. The parables of Jesus are exactly analogous. Whether or not there really was a good Samaritan is irrelevant to the point of Jesus' story: the precept of universal charity. Similarly it is entirely irrelevant whether there actually was a Deluge or a Noah. Certainly we have no evidence in geological history for such a universal flood. True, the Tigris and Euphrates rivers did flood at times as shown by successive layers of sediment in the area. But all were local floods.

Perhaps one of these local floods, more extreme than the rest, gave rise to the "universal Deluge" myth. Sir Leonard Woolley (1880-1960), excavating near Ur in the years 1929 and 1930, found an eleven-foot-deep deposit of silt between evidences of human occupation. He speculated that a deposit of such depth could have come from a flooding of the entire Mesopotamian region (perhaps as much as 30,000 square miles) to a depth of 26 feet. Survivors of this flood may have loaded onto their boats with them some of their domestic animals. Certainly the idea that representatives of all the animals on the earth entered and were preserved from drowning in the small quarters of an ark lacks plausibility. But, as noted, there is no reason to look for plausibility in a scientific basis or explanation for the details of the Deluge story. We are *not* asked to accept on divine faith that there was a universal Deluge. In fact, those who claim that the details must be true and must be believed because the word of God is infallible are quite mistaken. Divine inspiration, i.e., the charism to write down only what God wished written down, is not identical with the charism of infallibility. Infallibility extends only to the contents the Sacred Writer reports as revealed by God, and, as we saw before, does not extend to the means the Sacred Writer used to report these contents. In their reports, the Sacred Writers clearly made use of concepts, views, and even myths current in their cultural milieu to express the content of God's revelation.

Faith and science when each stays in its own area of competence do not and should not contradict each other. The area of natural science is natural phenomena and its competence is to explain them by natural forces. The primary paradigm of all natural science is that all natural phenomena can be explained by natural forces. To invoke some preternatural or supernatural force to explain some as yet unexplained natural phenomenon is to step outside this paradigm and is not acceptable to natural scientists. Attempts to explain natural phenomena as yet unexplained by natural causes by appealing to some intervention by God (the God-of-the-gaps) has been repeatedly shown to be mistaken. But explanations made by natural scientists as scientists cannot and should not go into the ultimate causes and purposes of natural phenomena. So scientific explanations cannot give answers to questions like these: "What is the ultimate source or origin of the universe and what it contains?" "What is the ultimate source of the regularities and laws that govern the world and make it a cosmos and not a chaos?" "Why, for what purpose, does the world exist?" "What is man's ultimate destiny?" Such questions may find partial answers from the efforts of philosophers using their powers of natural reason. These efforts are beyond the intellects of many humans. Christians believe that God has revealed their answers in ever increasing clarity to the prophets and holy persons of past ages. They believe that the clearest divine revelation was made to mankind by Jesus Christ. This divine revelation is accessible only by faith. In the Christian view, faith is a supernatural gift, one that man cannot attain by his own efforts but must be given by God. With this gift, man is able to know as true all the answers to the ultimate questions of existence given by God. But note again that God has not revealed scientific explanations for natural phenomena in the universe. Humans are left to their own resources to push these explanations as far as possible.

It has taken a long time for theologians to realize this fact. Their most conspicuous failure was their attempt to silence Galileo for defending the heliocentric theory proposed by Copernicus in opposition to the geocentric theory of the Aristotelians. Galileo's evidences were not convincing enough to compel assent and theologians thought that Scripture taught as divinely revealed and therefore infallible that the sun revolved around the earth. For example, one reads in the Scriptures that at the prayer of Joshua (Jos 10:12-14) the sun remained motionless in the sky until the Israelites overcame in battle their enemies the Amorites. In vain, Galileo pointed out that God's revelation was not concerned with astronomy but with man's supernatural destiny. He was forbidden to defend the heliocentric theory in his writings and was subjected to house arrest. On October 31, 1992, Pope John Paul II officially rehabilitated Galileo, declaring him a better theologian than the ones who had insisted on his condemnation. These had failed to distinguish God's word in the Bible from the way it was expressed. The Pope then went on to set forth some guidelines for the future handling of such disputes in the Catholic Church, guidelines which clearly respect the competence of science in scientific matters and of religion in matters of the spirit: "The 'Galileo case' teaches us that different branches of knowledge call for different methods, each of which brings out various aspects of reality."

If you think that nobody today would fail to make this

19

distinction between scientific fact and revealed truth, though, you are mistaken. A significant body of Christians, especially in the United States, insist on the literal interpretation of the Scriptures as fundamental to Christian religious faith. Fundamentalists believe that the answers to the questions of man's origin and moral obligations have been taken over in school curricula by the secular humanists who wish to eliminate any divine being or purpose as a concern of man and to substitute man himself as the sole measure of what is right and true, the master of his own fate. Fundamentalists see the influence of the secular humanists in the prominence given to evolution in biology and other science courses taught in the public schools. Since fundamentalists realize that it would be impossible to remove the subject of evolution from public school curricula, they have tried to require by law the simultaneous teaching of "scientific creationism." Their strategy has been to propose that the "theory of divine creation" is just as scientific as the "theory of evolution." Attempts by fundamentalists in Arkansas and Louisiana to have laws enacted embodying their strategy have been set aside by the U.S. Supreme Court on the grounds that such laws violate the First Amendment of the Constitution by promoting a particular religious doctrine. Fundamentalists now concentrate their efforts on local school boards, libraries, parents, and teachers to influence the selection and content of school books in favor of "creation science."

Through the years there have always been others who, unlike the fundamentalists, accept all of modern science's findings yet attempt to find references to them in the Genesis accounts, especially in the first chapter. One recent attempt is by William Lee Stokes, author of *The Genesis Answer: A Scientist's Testament for Divine Creation*. This example of "concordism," the reconciliation of the details of the Genesis account with the discoveries of modern science is perhaps the most complete and best informed. But all attempts at concordism suppose that Genesis, because it

20

is divinely inspired, is revealing true, detailed information about nature. This approach cannot be defended. In the case of Scripture, the medium is *not* the message!

## SUGGESTED READINGS

1. Eve, Raymond and Francis B. Harrold, *The Creationist Movement in Modern America* (New Haven, CT: Twayne, 1991).

2. Hanson, Robert W., "Introduction: Science or Belief, a False Dichotomy," pp. 1-9 in *Science and Creation: Geological, Theological, and Educational Perspectives*, Robert W. Hanson, ed. (New York, NY: Macmillan, 1986).

3. McMullin, Ernan, ed., *Galileo, Man of Science* (New York, NY: Basic Books, 1967).

4. Numbers, Ronald L., *The Creationists: The Evolution of Scientific Creationism* (New York, NY: Alfred A. Knopf, 1992).

5. Stokes, William L., *The Genesis Answer: A Scientist's Testament for Divine Creation* (Englewood Cliffs, NJ: Prentice-Hall, 1984).

6. Thomas, D. Winton, ed., *Documents form Old Testament Times* (New York, NY: Harper & Row, 1958).

# CHAPTER 4

# The Creation Accounts in Genesis

Today Scripture scholars have achieved great advances in understanding how the first five books of the Bible (the Pentateuch) were put together and what the purposes of the authors were. Much light on details has come from study of the beliefs and customs of the pagan contemporaries of the Biblical personages, as preserved in literary and archaeological remains. The Pentateuch records the election of Abraham and his descendants, the Israelites, as a people specially chosen to preserve the worship of the one true God. It records the acceptance by the Israelites of this covenant and their successes and failures in living up to it. Since its emphasis and guiding motif is to trace God's dealings with man, the Pentateuch is not history in the secular sense but a special kind of history, "sacred history," and cannot be justly evaluated and critiqued by standards appropriate to secular history.

The actual writing down of this history came comparatively late. Oral traditions preceded: the experiences and activities of Abraham, Isaac, Jacob, Joseph, Moses, Joshua, and so forth, were first told as stories, perhaps as the people gathered around a campfire. They were handed down, probably with some alterations as each storyteller dramatized an event. Thus we should not look for strict accuracy and agreement in details, as if the people involved were modern historians. The emphasis was on the point of each story. Scholars, in closely examining the Pentateuch as finally written down as we have it today, can distinguish several main traditions that were combined in the final version by a priest redactor working in the 6th century B.C. Even for the unsophisticated reader, chapters one and two of Genesis can be easily recognized as presenting the creation story in two different versions, each coming from a different source or tradition. One of these is the "J" tradition, so-called because it names God Yahweh, in German Jahveh. The creation account in the second chapter of Genesis comes from the "J" tradition. The "P" tradition, so-called because it includes the material supplied by the priest redactor himself to the Pentateuch, is the source of the creation account given in the first chapter of Genesis.

We have good reason to accept the basic historicity of the material in Genesis which begins with the call of Abraham in chapter 12. The social, juridical, political, geographical, and religious conditions described in this material are the same as are known today, from study of literary and archaeological remains, to prevail in the area in the second millennium B.C. The idea that an imaginative later writer could invent this material lacks credibility. However the earlier material of Genesis, especially that of the two creation accounts, does not appear to be based on historical sources in the ordinary sense. Certainly no one witnessed the actual creation. The peoples among whom the Israelites lived all had stories describing the origin of the world and man. It should not be surprising that the Israelites prefixed to their account of God's dealings with them as the chosen people an account of how their God created the world and especially humankind and how the first human beings behaved toward their Creator. Some scholars think that the author of Genesis from its beginning to the fifth verse of the second chapter used as a model of the creation events the version current in Babylon at his time.

He was well acquainted with that version since the Israelites had spent forty years in captivity there.

However, when we compare the Israelite with the Babylonian version, we find tremendous and essential differences. The Babylonian account written down in the epic *Enuma elish* ("When on high," its opening words) is a very complicated story. It begins with the two beings already in existence, Apsu (male) and Tiamat (female) generating a series of god descendants. These by their noisy revelries offend Apsu, who decides on their destruction but he is killed by one of them, Ea, the god of wisdom, spells and incantations. Tiamat, incited by Kingu, one of the dragons of chaos, seeks vengeance for her husband, but she in turn is overcome by the son of Ea, Marduk. Marduk cuts the body of Tiamat in two, and one half he makes into the sky. There he positions the sun, moon, and the stars. Out of the other half, he forms the earth. Finally Marduk directs Ea to form human beings out of the blood of Kingu.

The contrast of the Genesis account with the Babylonian account is obvious. The most fundamental difference is in the religious concepts behind the two accounts. The Babylonian story borrows its pantheon of gods from the Sumerians, non-Semitic predecessors of the Babylonians. These gods are personifications of various aspects of nature. Thus Apsu and Tiamat rule the seas, Anu the sky, Ea the earth. The Genesis account knows only one God, who forms the seas, the heavens, and the earth. The Babylonian account is a colorful tale of intrigue and struggle for dominance between the gods, ending with the exaltation of Marduk, the city-god of Babylon, as preeminent among the host of gods. The Genesis account knows no rival to the one God: the Creator is supreme and creates by His mere word. The division of God's creative work into six days with a seventh day devoted to "rest" probably reflects the later Israelite custom of working six days and then enjoying the next (seventh) day as a day of rest. The Babylonian account devotes relatively little space to the creative activities of Marduk, whereas the Genesis account is entirely given over to God's creating work.

The author of the Genesis account was aware of the Babylonian account but wished to substitute for it a creation story that agreed with the revelation of the one true God made to the Israelites from the time of Abraham on. The sequence of events described is the product of the author's desire to put order into his account and has no other meaning than as a literary device. Thus he first describes the separation of light from darkness, the separation of the waters above and below by the "firmament," and the separation of the dry land from the sea. Then he describes the population of these realms: the sky by sun, moon, and stars; the waters by sea creatures; the dry land by all manner of land animals and finally by human beings. Thus the objection that he represents God as creating light before the sources of light (sun, moon, stars) has no value.

Whether God created by evolution (a natural process) or not would have been irrelevant to the author and was a question that he could not have even conceived as a problem. He asserts nothing about it.

The second creation account (Genesis 2:5ff.) obviously differs from the first account already described. Thus, for example, in the second account human beings are created before the "land animals and the birds of heaven," whereas in the first, human beings are created after them. In the first, the emphasis is on God creating order out of chaos, resulting in the cosmos as conceived by the ancients, with human beings constituting God's crowning work. In the second, the emphasis is on the history of man's primordial relationship with God. In describing these early events, the author wishes to propose the origin or cause of man's situation as he knew it. He puts his explanation in the form of the story of Adam and Eve. In considering the details of the story, we must carefully distinguish what is asserted by the author from the details of the story. Thus efforts of some scholars to pin-point the locale of the garden of Eden was a useless exercise. When God is said to form the first man from the dust of the earth and to breathe into his nostrils the breath of life, the author is merely using a conception of the mode of human origin already found in Egyptian and Babylonian myths. He is not asserting that God acted like a potter in making man, but only that man was the special object of God's creative activity. *How* His activity was exercised is not asserted. The author certainly knew nothing of a possible evolutionary origin of man and so could not be denying such a possibility. Similarly, when the author represents God as forming from Adam's rib his feminine partner Eve, he may be expressing in a vivid way the essential equality intended by God for man and woman. In the author's time woman occupied an inferior and even debased position with respect to man. The author may be saying that in the beginning this condition did not exist and was not intended by God.

## SUGGESTED READINGS

1. Bergant, Dianne and Carroll Stuhlmueller, "Creation According to the Old Testament," pp. 153-175 in *Evolution and Creation*, Ernan McMullin, ed. (Notre Dame, IN: University of Notre Dame Press, 1985).

2. Clifford, Richard J., S.J., "Creation in the Hebrew Bible," pp. 151-170 in *Physics, Philosophy, and Theology: A Common Quest for Understanding*, R.J. Russell, W.R. Stoeger, S.J., and G.V. Coyne, S.J., eds. (Notre Dame, IN: University of Notre Dame Press, 1988).

3. McKenzie, John L., *Myths and Realities: Studies in Biblical Theology* (Milwaukee, WI: Bruce, 1963).

4. Pritchard, J.B., ed., *Ancient Near Eastern Texts Relating to the Old*

*Testament*, 3rd ed. (Princeton, NJ: Princeton University Press, 1969).

5. Skehan, James W., "The Age of the Earth, of Life, and of Mankind: Geology and Biblical Theology versus Creationism," pp. 10-32 in *Science and Creation: Geological, Theological, and Educational Perspectives*, Robert W. Hanson, ed. (New York, NY: Macmillan, 1986).

6. Thomas, D. Winton, ed., *Documents from Old Testament Times* (New York, NY: Harper & Row, 1958).

# CHAPTER 5

# Adam and Eve: Our First Parents?
# Monogenism vs. Polygenism

I s the author of the second creation account given in the second chapter of Genesis asserting that mankind began with just one pair, Adam and Eve, so that all subsequent humans go back by physical generation to these as the first parents of the human race (monogenism)? In the account of the creation of the first humans, the word "adam" is first used not as a proper name, but rather means "the man" ('adh am from the Hebrew 'adh am ah meaning "earth"). Later on the author uses it to name the first male, Adam. Adam calls his female counterpart Eve "the mother of all those who live." Here the author of Genesis appears to have in mind a derivation from the Hebrew verb ha va "to live." The author was not directly concerned to defend the concept of monogenism against the concept of polygenism (the origin of mankind from several first parents).

Why then are Christians so concerned to defend monogenism against polygenism? The answer is found in the doctrine of "original sin." Adam and Eve committed the first or original sin when they, the first humans, ate the fruit of the tree of the knowledge of good and evil in the garden of Eden, despite God's explicit command not to do so. Their punishment was to be expelled from the garden, where they had enjoyed a familiar relationship with God, to live a life of hardship and toil ending with death. Before their loss of innocence, their animal and rational appetites were in harmony. Now they had to struggle to keep their animal passions from dominating them. The author of Genesis implies this when he says that after their sin they realized that they were naked and covered themselves with skins.

According to some Scriptural exegetes, the author of this account in Genesis composed the story of the "fall" to provide an explanation for the condition of mankind as known to him: alienated from God, sunk in sin, and doomed to die. The author represents the sin of Adam and Eve as the origin of this state of affairs. He was composing "etiological history," a story giving the cause in the past for a situation present to him. Other exegetes take a more traditional approach. According to them, the account in Genesis is historical in the usual sense. It relates events that actually occurred at the dawn of human existence with a definite pair, Adam and Eve, as the principal protagonists. Pope John Paul II closely follows this traditional approach in his catechetical instructions. Regarding original sin, the new *Catechism of the Catholic Church* states: "The account of the 'fall,' Original Sin, uses figurative language, but affirms a fundamental event, a deed that took place at the beginning of the history of human beings... [A]ll human history is marked by the original fault freely committed by our first parents" [390].

The doctrine of "original sin" maintains that Adam's sin is passed down to all humans after him. The idea is that Adam as progenitor of all humans acted as representative of them so that all descendants of Adam and Eve share in his sin and its consequences. St. Paul seems to be quite explicit about this. In Romans 5:12-19, he draws a parallel between the roles of Adam and Christ in salvation history. Paul observes that as through Adam, sin, death, and "condemnation" became the fate of all mankind, so through Christ forgiveness of sin, eternal life, and justification were restored to mankind. The argument from this text and similar ones in Paul is that as Christ was a single individual, as no one doubts, so Adam also must have been a single individual. This seems to be the obvious conclusion from Paul's statement and excludes polygenism. This is explicitly stated by Pope Pius XII in his encyclical *Humani Generis*. He wrote: ". . . the faithful cannot embrace that opinion which maintains either that after Adam there existed on this earth true men who did not take their origin through natural generation from him as the first parent of them all, or that Adam represents a certain number of first parents. Now *it is in no way apparent* [italics added] how such an opinion can be reconciled with that which the sources of revealed truth and the documents of the Teaching Authority of the Church propose with regard to original sin, which proceeds from sin actually committed by an individual Adam and which through generation is passed on to all and is in everyone as his own."

Some theologians, for example Karl Rahner, do not regard this statement of Pius XII as an *infallible definition* of Catholic dogma, which would make "monogenism" an article of Catholic faith. Pius XII based his exclusion of polygenism on the inability of reconciling polygenism with the Church's official teaching about the transmission of original sin. If this present inability could be overcome in the future, say, by some modified form of polygenism or some different but acceptable interpretation of the Church's teaching on original sin, polygenism could be accepted by Catholics. It is certain that Pius XII did not wish to proscribe research on the question with the object of throwing more light on it. In an address to Carmelite Fathers in 1951, the year after his encyclical, Pius denied that he "wanted to prevent the investigations which the progress of doctrine demands."

What light does science throw on the question of monogenism? In the first place, investigations of anthropologists establish that all present day humans belong to one species.

31

Obviously they differ in a number of respects which form the basis of racial distinctions. The Greenland Eskimo with his short chunky build contrasts sharply with the African Masai with his very tall slender build. Besides these obvious external differences in build, color of skin, and so forth, the races differ in the relative incidences of various internal biochemical properties, as for instance their blood types due to different antigens present on their red blood cells. But despite these differences, all the races, as far as is known, can mate to produce fertile progeny. Thus they fulfill the critical test for belonging to one species, that is, no reproductive barrier exists between the races. Examination of their chromosome complements, the bearers of the hereditary factors, the genes, show that all races agree in having the same number of chromosomes, viz., 23 pairs. The only known difference is in the size of their Y chromosomes, e.g., large in Japanese, small in Australian aborigines. From these facts which establish that modern humans form one species, anthropologists conclude that all humans living today go back to one origin.

While there is general agreement among anthropologists that all the races of modern man evolved from a preceding primitive human, *Homo erectus*, there is dispute about how this evolution of races came about. One theory, the "Regional Continuity Theory" is that as *Homo erectus* spread over Africa and Eurasia, separate populations gradually evolved in response to selection for adaptation to the demands of their different environments into the different races. The races remained still one species because genes continued to be exchanged between the different populations and no reproductive barriers arose. The separate populations of *Homo erectus* evolved by parallel evolution those characteristics by which we recognize modern *Homo sapiens*, viz., especially the enlarged brain and the less robust skeleton. According to this theory, *Homo sapiens* evolved from several stems of *Homo erectus* in different areas of the earth (polyphyletic evolution). As evidence for this theory, its backers point to a series of skulls of ancient *Homo erectus* specimens from different world regions which show resemblances to modern human skulls from the same regions. For example, some *Homo erectus* crania from China show similarities to modern Chinese.

The other main theory, the "Out-of-Africa Theory," maintains that *Homo sapiens* evolved from a population of *Homo erectus* in only one place, viz., Africa, and then spread out as *Homo sapiens* into Europe, Asia, and Australia (monophyletic evolution). In these different environments, distinctive racial characteristics evolved. Paleontological evidence for an African origin of *Homo sapiens* includes fossils from the Klasies River mouth deposits in Africa. These, though completely modern in all respects, are tentatively dated as being between 80,000 and 115,000 years old. Genetic evidence comes from the analyses of both nuclear and mitochondrial DNA sequences from people from various ethnic groups in Africa, Asia, and Europe. Sequences from people of African origin show significantly greater variation than sequences from people of non-African origin. The inference drawn is that modern man must have existed longer in Africa than elsewhere to accumulate the greater genetic variation. This conclusion favors an African point of origin for *Homo sapiens*.

Mitochondria (organelles in the cytoplasm generating energy needed for metabolism) are inherited only through the maternal line, and are not diluted with paternal mitochondrial DNA. The male's sperm does not transmit mitochondria to the fertilized egg (zygote). As mentioned in the previous paragraph, the mitochondrial DNA (mt DNA) of African origin shows greater variation than mt DNA of non-African origin. Attempts to arrange the mt DNA in an evolutionary sequence have pointed to the oldest sequence as African. In 1987 biochemist Allan C. Wilson proposed that all living human beings had inherited mitochondrial DNA from a single woman. Using statistical and computer analysis of mitochondrial DNA from people of various ethnic groups and assuming a slow, constant rate of genetic mutation, Wilson concluded that the oldest mitochondrial DNA was African and that the mitochondrial DNA of all humans stemmed from one woman who lived about 200,000 years ago. His work did not suggest that this woman was the only female ancestor alive 200,000 years ago. Not surprisingly the media sensationalized this conclusion as the discovery of mitochondrial Eve. Unfortunately the methods used to arrange the mt DNA in a phylogenetic sequence have been severely criticized as erroneous. A further study using a more diverse mitochondrial sampling and supporting Wilson's theory was released by members of Wilson's laboratory in 1991, but other computer analyses of mt DNA samples have indicated that several different trees may be constructed from the same data and that the order in which the DNA samples are analyzed affects the results. So the media now announce that it is time to write the obituary of mitochondrial Eve. Fresh molecular studies with mt DNA, while silent on the geographical origin of "Eve," confirm her origin as fairly recent. One estimate gives a range from 126,000 to 253,000 years before the present. So, adapting a quotation from Mark Twain, the media reports of the death of mitochondrial Eve have been greatly exaggerated. The paleontological evidence still favors an African origin of modern *Homo sapiens*.

Leaving more on the data and speculations of the paleontologists and anthropologists on the origin of modern man to later chapters, we turn to the view of the geneticists on the origin of species. The field of population genetics is particularly pertinent here for the light it throws on the evolution of species. Briefly, species arise either over geological time by divergences from a previously existing species and ending up by replacing it, or in geographic space by a separation of one interbreeding population into two or more separate populations no longer interbreeding. In both modes, changes in gene complements by various means (gene mutations and/or chromosomal mutations) are basic. If these changes are adaptive to the particular environment in which the original population of organisms is present, they may spread through the population by the process called "natural selection." Some of these changes may bring about reproductive isolation. When they do, we have the origin of new species. Important in this brief sketch of how species arise is the role of the population. The hereditary changes leading to a new species occur in a population of interbreeding organisms and the new species arises out of it in a gradual process. True, geneticists are aware that new species can arise relatively suddenly in organisms with more than two sets of chromosomes by the process called polyploidy, especially allopolyploidy.

Allopolyploidy occurs when the chromosome complements (genomes) of two different species are combined by a fortuitous cross-fertilization and then are duplicated. The process can result in the instant emergence of a new species, reproductively compatible in crosses with itself but incompatible in crosses with its parent species. The process is well-known in plants and is responsible for the origin of some plant species, including some economically important to man, for example, cotton. The process is not likely to succeed in animals which sexually reproduce because it would bring about imbalances of the sex chromosomes with consequent infertility. As far as the origin of man is concerned, inspection of his chromosome complement shows no indication that polyploidy was ever involved.

Another possibility for the sudden emergence of man with no dependence on his population comes from the theory championed by Richard Goldschmidt of the "hopeful monster." In this theory a sudden drastic rearrangement of the genes in the genome could bring about a new constellation of properties in the organism making it very different from others in its population. This theory has gained little favor from geneticists for the various problems it creates, the most serious of which is how this new organism could reproduce since it would be very different in its chromosomal constitution from any others in its population.

It seems fair to conclude that geneticists find it difficult to conceive of the origin of man as involving a single pair, one man and one woman. All their theories and observations on the origin of a new biological species involve changes in populations. If man is the result of the ordinary process of evolution, his origin is to be found in a group of individuals evolving together in response to the demands of their environment, and not in just one pair. Do science and faith here contradict each other?

Resolution of this apparent contradiction can be found in a distinction: evolution of proto-humans proceeded according to the usual mode just described for the evolution of any species but the origin of the first *true humans* must be ascribed to a special intervention of God in the process of evolution. Why is a special divine intervention needed? The ordinary natural processes of evolution cannot bridge the gap between proto-humans, no matter how clever and human-like, and true humans (*Homo sapiens*) endowed with spiritual souls, abstract reasoning, and free wills. In chapter eleven we will discuss in detail the uniqueness of true humans and also the transit from proto-humans to true humans. The difference between manlike creatures (e.g., apes) and man is not merely a matter of degree (a quantitative difference) but a matter of life on an entirely different plane (a qualitative difference).

In light of these considerations we should not be surprised to find God as described in Genesis 2 intervening in a special way in the creation of the first humans. Thus what we would expect from philosophical considerations, we know also from revelation. That God's intervention focused on one pair (Adam and Eve) to give rise to mankind we could only know from revelation. To sum up our considerations: the origin of proto-humans involved polygenism, but the origin of true humans involved monogenism. In making this statement, we are faithful both to

36

modern science and to traditional faith. Their findings *do not* contradict each other.

## SUGGESTED READINGS

1. *Catechism of the Catholic Church*, Nos. 375-410, Most Rev. Christoph Schönborn, Gen. ed. (Boston, MA: St. Paul Editions, 1994).

2. Hogan, Richard M. and John M. Levoir, "Original Sin and the Providence of God," Ch. 3, esp. pp. 53-63 in *Faith for Today: Pope John Paul II's Catechetical Teachings* (New York, NY: Doubleday, 1988).

3. Gibbons, Ann, "Mitochondrial Eve: Wounded but Not Dead Yet," in *Science*, v. 257: pp. 873-875, 1992.

4. Gibbons, Ann, "Mitochondrial Eve Refuses to Die," *Science*, v. 259: pp. 1249-1250, 1993.

5. Lewin, Roger, "Species Questions in Modern Human Origins," *Science*, v. 243: pp. 1666-1667, 1989.

6. Pius XII, Address to Carmelite Fathers in *Acta Apostolicae Sedis*, v. 43: p. 758, 1951.

7. Pius XII, *Humani Generis*, encyclical (New York, NY: Paulist Press, 1950).

8. Rahner, Karl, "Theological Reflections on Monogenism," in *Theological Investigations*, 1: pp. 229-296 (Baltimore, MD: Helicon Press, 1961).

9. Rahner, Karl, "Evolution and Original Sin," *Concilium*, v. 26 (New York, NY: Paulist Press, 1967).

10. Rahner, Karl, "The Sin of Adam," in *Theological Investigations*, IX: pp. 247-262 (New York, NY: Seabury Press, 1974).

11. Renchens, Henricus, Ch. 22, "Monogenism and Original Sin," pp. 244-252, and Ch. 23, "The Origin of the Monogenistic Idea," pp. 253-262 in *Israel's Concept of the Beginning: The Theology of Genesis 1-3*, trans. Charles Napier (New York, NY: Herder and Herder, 1964).

12. Smulders, Piet, "Monogenism," Appendix IV, pp. 188-195 in *The Design of Teilhard de Chardin* (Westminster, MD: Newman Press, 1967).

13. Stringer, Christopher and P. Andries, "Genetic and Fossil Evidence for the Origin of Modern Humans," in *Science*, v. 239: pp. 1263-1268, 1988.

14. Stringer, Christopher, "The Emergence of Modern Humans," in *Scientific American*, pp. 98-104, December, 1990.

# CHAPTER 6

# Origin and Age of the Earth

The evolution of life took place on the planet earth as an historical process always affected by the conditions prevailing on it. But the evidence is compelling that the earth itself has its own history that began in the remote past at a particular stage in the evolution of the universe. The point of time at which the earth began to exist sets an upper limit for the time available for the evolution of life on it. We are therefore concerned here with two questions: "How did the earth originate?" and "How old is it?"

For an answer to our first question, the origin of the earth, we turn to the theories of the astrophysicists. They begin with a stage perhaps 10 to 20 billion years ago when all the matter of the universe was concentrated into a small space extremely dense and many millions of degrees hot. Under these conditions, of the elementary nuclear particles, only neutrons, protons, and electrons could exist. As the temperature fell, neutrons and protons joined to form nuclei, first of the lighter elements such as hydrogen and helium, and later of heavier elements such as lithium. When the density of the condensed matter became maximum and repulsion forces exceeded those favoring compression, the primitive "atom" exploded. This was the "Big Bang" of the astrophysicists. This primordial explosion continues to this day (!) for the billions of galaxies populating the universe are "flying" away from each other at fantastic speeds. This explains what has been known for some time: the light waves reaching us from the stars in the receding galaxies are lengthened and thus produce a Doppler effect on their spectra, a shift to the red end. A relic of the "Big Bang" is the background microwave radiation pervading the universe discovered by Arno Penzias and Robert Wilson in 1965. Their discovery made the theory that a "Big Bang" triggered the evolution of the universe acceptable to astrophysicists for the first time.

At first the expanding universe was composed of a hot gas consisting of the newly formed atoms. As the temperature fell to a few thousand degrees, elements in the gas with high melting points condensed into a fine dust floating in a mixture of hydrogen and helium. At first uniformly distributed, random movements of the dust particles brought about condensations: the protogalaxies. Once formed, these protogalaxies would be maintained by Newtonian gravity forces. These condensations would be endowed with rotation at various speeds by the condensation process. The protogalaxies at first consisted only of cool gas with no stars present. The motion of the rapidly rotating gas in a protogalaxy would be turbulent, with local eddies of material. The eddying material would produce here and there local compressions. Gravity would promote further contraction of this material into individual dense gas spheres. As contraction proceeded, the temperature of the gas spheres increased to the point that their surfaces would emit, first, heat rays, and then the wavelengths of visible light. At a certain stage of contraction, the core temperature of these beginning stars would reach the ignition point of thermonuclear reactions and the stars as known today would be born.

One of the stars so formed in our galaxy was our sun. As the sun was formed in a turbulent eddy in its protogalaxy, it was first surrounded by a spherical rotating envelope of dust particles prevented by their large angular velocities from falling into the central solar condensation. At first spherical, the envelope consisted of particles moving rapidly in different planes and in different directions. These particles would collide with each other with the result that eventually they would force each other to adopt the same direction of motion in the same flat plane. In this disk, due to differential attractions of gravity, local condensations of dust particles would arise: the origin of the separate planets rotating in the same plane about the sun. One of these planets was our earth.

In the above scenario, I have given an outline of a widely accepted theory on the origin of the universe — including our earth — originally sketched (1948) by the astrophysicist George Gamow. More details on this theory can be found in the Suggested Readings listed at the end of this chapter. Whether this theory or any other is correct or not in all or none of its details, it appears that natural science can provide a plausible explanation for the origin of the universe, employing what is known today about matter and energy and the physical laws governing their interactions.

Does this scientific explanation of the origin of the universe including our earth contradict the scriptural accounts given in Genesis? When we remember what has been repeatedly emphasized, that Scripture is a religious document telling us about God and our relations to Him and that it is not a scientific account, we find no contradiction. Scripture tells us that God "made heaven and earth," i.e., that He is their ultimate cause and origin. It is *not* revealing how He made it. The scientific explanation we have given above is a fascinating account of how He could have made it. Note, I say, "could have made it." It would be very foolish to make our belief in God as the Creator of heaven and earth (the universe) depend on a scientific theory no matter how probable. We do *not* believe in God as the Creator of the universe because

41

science can give us an attractive account of how creation may have come about. We believe because we trust in God's word in this matter.

Astronomers have shown that the expanding universe extends already over billions of light years. In this expanse they have discovered billions of galaxies, of which our own, the Milky Way galaxy, is only one representative. In this galaxy, our sun appears as an ordinary star and our earth as one of the planets orbiting about it. These considerations have led some to ridicule the idea that a human being has any significance in the universe. In response to this view a Christian believer can say that one human being capable of knowledge and love is incomparably more significant and more important than any number of celestial objects lacking consciousness and free will. Also it is not impossible that rational beings similar to us occupy planets suitable for their emergence and survival that according to some astronomers are to be found in good number in the various galaxies. If this speculation is true, the galaxies in the immense reaches of the universe would have a role other than providing, as they do, rich material for contemplation and wonder for us earthlings.

Turning now to the second question about the earth, we ask, "How old is it?" Evolution admittedly is a slow process and therefore required an immense amount of time for life to emerge and then evolve to the present profusion of living things. The current controversy between evolutionists whether evolution proceeded gradually or whether it proceeded in spurts ("punctuated evolution") does not affect this conclusion. So we wish to know how much time was available for evolution to proceed. To answer this question, we must know the age of the earth.

Until a few decades ago, any scientific answer was necessarily indefinite: the earth must be very old, many millions of years old, to allow the many changes in its surface (the uplifting of mountain ranges, the formation of deep canyons, the deposition of hundreds of feet of sedimentary rocks, the present position of the continents, and so forth) to take place. Now a fairly precise answer comes from the discovery that certain radioactive elements disintegrate at a constant rate, unaffected by chemical reactions, to daughter elements. The rate at which this change takes place for any particular radioactive element can be determined (its "half-life," i.e., the time required to convert half of a given amount to the daughter element). For instance, uranium 238 disintegrates to produce helium and lead 206. The half-life of uranium 238 is 4,510,000,000 years. To date the age of a rock formation, the relative amounts of the parent and daughter elements present are determined. Assuming that when the rock was formed only the parent element was present and knowing its half-life, the amount of the daughter element formed measures the age of the rock formation. Using this method, the oldest rocks on the earth have been dated as 3.8 billion years old. Further information comes from dating the age of the stony meteorites that have fallen on the earth. If we assume that these meteorites were formed at the same time as the earth in the process that gave rise to our solar system described earlier in this chapter, the earth must also be at least 4.5 billion years old. A still further refinement comes from the computation of how long it took to form the earth's supply of lead 207 from its parent uranium. This calculation gives the age of the earth as 5.6 billion years. The results of these various calculations taken from Skehan (Suggested Reading No. 3) tell us that the earth is no younger than 4.5 billion and probably no older than 5.6 billion years. This amount of time seems sufficient to allow evolution to have taken place, including the origin of living things from non-living materials.

These scientific studies disprove calculations of the age of the earth based on the information in the Old Testament, viz., the ages of persons given in genealogies and the length of intervals between some important events. The ages assigned to the lives of some very early personages (the classic example is Methuselah: 969 years) cannot be taken seriously and reflect the exaggerations of the storytellers of the time. The length of intervals given (e.g., 430 years for the stay of the Israelites in Egypt, 480 years from the exodus of the Israelites from Egypt to the building of Solomon's temple) are more credible. Yet adding together all these time intervals taken from the Hebrew text of the Old Testament gives only 4163 years from the creation of the world to the birth of Christ, obviously in contradiction to the immense age of the earth based on the results of scientific investigations. As we have noted earlier (Chapter 4), scriptural fundamentalists, despite this contradiction, hold on to a very short age of the earth because they believe in the literal truth of everything contained in Scripture. To defend their position, they attack the accuracy of the scientific calculations.

## SUGGESTED READINGS

1. Hawking, Stephen W., *A Brief History of Time from the Big Bang to Black Holes* (New York, NY: Bantam Press, 1988).

2. Gamow, George, *The Creation of the Universe* (New York, NY: New American Library of World Literature, 1952).

3. Skehan, James W., "The Age of the Earth, of Life, and of Mankind: Geology and Biblical Theology versus Creationism," pp. 1-32 in *Science and Creation: Geological, Theological, and Educational Perspectives*, Robert W. Hanson, ed. (New York, NY: Macmillan, 1986).

4. Weinberg, Steven, *The First Three Minutes* (New York, NY: Basic Books, 1977).

# CHAPTER 7

# The Origin of Life

E ven the simplest living thing existing today, e.g., a bacterium, is actually a very complex entity composed of thousands of chemical compounds organized in a very complex pattern, carrying on many chemical processes (metabolism), and able to give rise to entities like itself (reproduction). No scientist thinks that such an entity could ever arise completely organized and living at once *de novo* from non-living materials. The probability of this happening is effectively zero. However, scientists have studied the possibility that a living cell might arise by a series of steps from non-living raw materials, with each step having some probability of occurring. The chemical compounds making up the living cell, principally proteins and nucleic acids, are themselves polymers of simpler units. The proteins are made up of amino acids and the nucleic acids are made up of nucleotides. Could these simpler subunits have arisen spontaneously under conditions prevailing in the first ages of the earth? Among these conditions, a key requirement is that the atmosphere contain no free oxygen. Any organic compound spontaneously synthesized would have been instantly degraded by free oxygen. So the primitive atmosphere must have had no free oxygen present, but with other gases such as hydrogen, methane, ammonia, carbon monoxide, carbon dioxide, and nitrogen present. Free oxygen would come much later as a by-product of photosynthesizing cells. With no oxygen in the atmosphere, there would have been no ozone present to absorb the ultraviolet radiation coming from the sun. This UV radiation could have been one source of the energy needed to join simpler compounds into amino acids, the basic units of proteins. Other possible sources of this required energy could have been electrical from lightning discharges, and thermal from the heat emitted by volcanoes and nuclear disintegrations of radioactive elements.

Stanley Miller and Harold Urey in 1953 sent an electrical spark discharge through a mixture of hydrogen, methane, ammonia, and water vapor. They found that four amino acids (glycine, glutamic acid, alanine, and aspartic acid) common in proteins were produced, along with many other molecules associated with life. In subsequent experiments they varied the gases (e.g., carbon monoxide or carbon dioxide for methane, nitrogen for ammonia) and ultraviolet radiation for the spark discharge, with similar results. In addition to the four amino acids already mentioned, they found eight others (leucine, isoleucine, serine, threonine, aspargine, lysine, phenylalanine, and tyrosine). These later experiments suppose a primitive atmosphere lacking methane and ammonia but containing carbon dioxide in place of methane as a carbon source and nitrogen gas instead of ammonia as a nitrogen source. Such an altered primitive atmosphere is favored by more recent studies of scientists. There is no doubt that under conditions probably present in the primitive earth atmosphere, amino acids, essential building blocks for proteins, can be readily synthesized. Nucleotides are the basic monomers (molecules that can be chemically bounded together as a unit) for nucleic acids, the other essential constituent of living material as existing today. Nucleotides consist of a five carbon sugar (ribose or deoxyribose) joined to an organic base (a purine or a pyrimidine) and to phosphate. In experiments simulating pre-biotic conditions, the five carbon sugar ribose, purines, and pyrimidines have been readily produced. Nucleosides (ribose joined to one of the purines or pyrimidines) have been synthesized only with difficulty, and at this writing so far no nucleotides (a nucleoside joined to phosphate).

Supposing as given the presence of amino acids and nucleotides, the next step in the chemical evolution of life would be their polymerization into proteins and nucleic acids. In the polymerization of proteins, a water molecule must be removed when one amino acid is joined to another, and energy is required. This reaction will not readily proceed in the aqueous medium presumably present on the pre-biotic earth. One solution of several proposed is that the polymerization proceeded in a pond being evaporated by solar heat. In 1965 Sidney Fox at the University of Miami showed that dry mixtures of amino acids would spontaneously polymerize when heated for a few hours. Polymers consisting of 200 or more amino acids have been produced by this method. Fox has speculated that amino acids formed in the primeval "soup" of the oceans could have washed up on volcanic cinder cones, evaporated to dryness, and then polymerized by the heat of the volcanoes into proteins. The pre-biotic polymerization of nucleotides to form nucleic acids with the correct chemical linkages is a much more difficult problem and remains unsolved.

All living cells are separated from their environment by a membrane absolutely necessary to keep the contents of the cell from being dispersed into the surrounding medium. Attempts to mimic this requirement have been made by the Russian biochemist A.I. Oparin and the American Sidney Fox. Fox warmed concentrated solutions of the polypeptides he had previously formed by heating a dry mixture of amino acids. Between 130 and 180 degrees Centigrade these polypeptides spontaneously aggregated into microspheres one or two micrometers in diameter.

These had a double-layered outer boundary resembling the double lipid layer of a true cell membrane. Under certain conditions the microspheres increased in size by including more of the polypeptide solution and even budded and divided in a manner superficially similar to the budding of bacteria. A few of the microsphere preparations showed a low degree of catalytic activity. For example, they could decompose glucose and function as esterases or peroxidases. Evidently the random combination of the amino acids in the polypeptides had brought about arrangements of side groups similar to those in the active sites of true enzymes. From the experiments of Fox and others we have gotten as far as experiments have mimicked the pre-biotic evolution of cells.

The differences between these crude models and the simplest cell existing today are truly immense. True cells have a complicated bilipid membrane in which are inserted numerous proteins involved in various functions such as the transfer of materials into the cell and the transduction of signals from the environment of the cell to the nuclear genes. All cells contain one or more enormous molecules of a nucleic acid, most often deoxyribonucleic acid (DNA), which constitute the genes coding for the proteins needed by the cell in its construction and functions, especially enzymes. Protein synthesis in a cell is an extremely complicated process involving transcription of the genes coding for each protein into an intermediary messenger ribonucleic acid (RNA) molecule, and the translation of this messenger RNA into the final polypeptide product. The nucleic acid genes along with certain proteins are assembled into one or more chromosomes. The activity of the genes is closely controlled by interactions of various regulatory molecules with specific sites on the genes. The chromosomes of eucaryotes are set off by a nuclear membrane from the surrounding cytoplasm. The cytoplasm is far from homogeneous. In eucaryotes it possesses a cytoskeleton made up of microtubules and contains

various complex organelles, the chief of which are the mitochondria and, in photosynthetic cells, the chloroplasts. Reproduction
of a cell is a complex process. As a preliminary it involves the
exact replication of the chromosomes so that each daughter cell
receives normally identical copies of the chromosomes present
in the mother cell.

A number of scientists continue to speculate on how such
a complex entity as the cell as it exists today could originate. One
problem they seek to solve is how the close reciprocal dependence of nucleic acids and proteins came about. Today proteins
including enzymes receive their essential basic structure as a
linear polymer of specific amino acids from a decoding of a
corresponding linear sequence of nucleotides in nucleic acid. But
the nucleic acid, which is autocatalytic, meaning it serves as a
template for a nucleic acid identical with it, depends for the
joining of the nucleotides making up its structure on enzymes,
very specific proteins. It is a chicken versus the egg situation:
which came first, the nucleic acid or the protein?

Cairn-Smith has proposed that microscopic crystals of
various kinds of clay containing small amounts of metallic ions
could absorb free amino acids or short polypeptides. These clay
particles according to him could grow and reproduce faithfully
their patterns of crystal imperfections and mineral inclusions.
Thus they could continue to promote the polymerization of
proteins. Some of these absorbed proteins might enzymatically
break down some of the proteins randomly formed by heat or
other means in the milieu and thus obtain a rich source of amino
acids for absorption to the clay template. These would allow the
particular clay-protein system to reproduce more rapidly than
other systems not so favored: the birth of a primitive natural
selection process. The next step would be to substitute nucleic
acids for the microscopic crystalline template. For this step
Bernal has proposed the absorption of nucleotides onto the
crystal next to the proteins or even on the proteins themselves.

Today almost all enzymes use nucleotides (co-enzymes) to provide energy for the breaking or making of chemical bonds. Thus these crystal-protein systems provided with nucleotides would be much more efficient in breaking down foreign polypeptides and thus would be able to reproduce faster. Eventually the protein-nucleotide combination would be freed from the clay crystalline substrate and be an independent entity. A next step would involve the enclosure of the system with a membrane-like coating.

In the early 1980's the surprising discovery was made that certain ribonucleic acid (RNA) molecules under special conditions act as enzymatic polymerases. This finding led to the speculation that the first molecules involved in the evolution of life were RNA rather than DNA (deoxyribonucleic acid) molecules. Strong support for this view has come from the 1992 experiments of Harry Noller and his group at the University of California, Santa Cruz. They have shown that it is the RNA in the ribosomes and not the proteins also present which catalyze the formation of bonds between successive amino acids in protein synthesis.

Much more detail on the various speculations on the origin of life can be obtained in the Suggested Readings for this chapter. My purpose in giving as much detail as I have given is to provide the reader with some appreciation of the lines of evidence supporting the speculations of the biochemists and biologists. Fundamental to all these speculations is the view that living things differ from non-living things primarily in their degree of organization, and the idea that their properties of replication, metabolism, etc., arise only from their complex organization. So in their speculations about the origin of life scientists have been concerned as to how this complex organization came about. In his 1993 book *The Origins of Order: Self-Organization and Selection in Evolution*, Stuart Kauffman explains how order can spontaneously arise in complex systems by the operation of general chemical and physical laws and provide a field for the operation of natural selection. The question can be raised as to whether all the properties, e.g., organismal properties of living things, are completely explained simply by complex organization. For the moment, we return to the question posed throughout this work: are these scientific speculations about the origin of life contrary to the beliefs of a Christian? Fundamentally these speculations propose a gradual evolution of life based on the chemical and physical properties of matter and favored by the particular environment provided by the state of the primitive earth. At first random factors played the only role. If some kinds of chemical "natural selection" had not arisen to favor the dominance of some of the chemical systems arising by chance, very probably no significant progress to life would have occurred. The time required to get all the chance factors acting together to form the simplest true cell would be so great as to make the occurrence of the event practically impossible. After the origin of the earth, dated as 4.6 billion years ago, chemical evolution proceeded for somewhat over a billion years. This follows from the age (3.2 - 3.6 billion years) of the earliest signs of life, microfossils resembling bacteria found in some sedimentary rocks of South Africa. This amount of time, around a billion years, is thought sufficient to allow the origin of simple cells by chemical evolution.

Scripture tells the Christian believer that God created all living things, plants and animals, but tells us nothing about how He created them. Thus, if living things did arise out of non-living things when their organization reached a level capable of vital activity including the ability to carry on metabolism and reproduction, the Christian believer considers this transition only possible because of potentialities with which the Creator endowed the non-living things. The Christian believer knows God as present and working in non-living things to keep them in existence and to sustain their activities. This presence and activity of God is not perceptible to the tools of the natural scientist and need not be taken in account in scientific explanations. The natural scientist rightly resents any recourse to a "Deus ex machina" in seeking an explanation of what he observes or has reason to think has happened in the sensible world accessible to him, including the origin of life. The Christian believer recognizes that any special intervention of God in the world He created and sustains, outside of the Creator's basic role as the ultimate ground of all existence and the author of the laws of nature which give direction to its evolution, is not to be assumed except for some very special reason, as in the case of miracles. Thus the natural scientist in the case of the origin of life should find no hindrance for his speculations from a Christian believer.

## SUGGESTED READINGS

1. Dyson, Freeman, *Origins of Life* (New York, NY: Cambridge University Press, 1986).

2. Dyson, Freeman, "Why Is Life So Complicated?", pp. 74-96 in *Infinite in All Directions* (New York, NY: Harper & Row, 1988).

3. Dyson, Freeman, "How Did Life Begin?", pp. 54-73 in *Infinite in All Directions* (New York, NY: Harper & Row, 1988).

4. Fox, S., ed., *The Origins of Prebiological Systems* (New York, NY: Academic Press, 1965).

5. Joyce, Gerald D., "RNA Evolution and the Origin of Life," *Nature*, v. 338: pp. 217-224, 1989.

6. Kasting, James F., "Earth's Early Atmosphere," *Science*, v. 259: pp. 920-926, 1993.

7. Kauffman, Stuart A., *The Origins of Order: Self-Organization and Selection in Evolution* (New York, NY: Oxford University Press, 1993).

8. Noller, Harry, "Ribosomal RNA and Translation," *Ann. Rev. Biochem.*, v. 60: pp. 191 ff., 1991.

9. Oparin, A., *Life: Its Nature, Origin, and Development*, Ann Synge, tr. (Edinburgh: Oliver & Boyd, 1961).

10. Pace, Norman R., "New Horizons for RNA Catalysis," *Science*, v.256: pp. 1402-1403, 1992.

11. Waldrop, M. Mitchell, "Finding RNA Makes Proteins Gives 'RNA World' a Big Boost," *Science*, v. 256: pp. 1396-1397, 1992.

# CHAPTER 8

# The Evidence for Evolution

I n preceding chapters we have learned that the authors of the scriptural accounts of creation were giving a religious message and not a scientific account of the events. They were given no special revelation about the way God brought about the visible creation. Therefore no argument against an evolutionary origin for creation can be based on Scripture. But in examining the theory of evolution from a scientific viewpoint, do we find elements that are opposed to the teachings of religious faith? Can one be an evolutionist and a Christian believer at the same time?

In answering this question, we will first consider the evidences for evolution and how cogent they are, and second, we will look at various theories about how evolution took place, in particular Darwin's theory of natural selection. It is especially in considering this second matter that we will come to grips with factors that might cause problems for Christian faith. Darwin himself originally was a believer and a member of the Anglican Church. Gradually he lost his faith in a personal God as he pondered over the evidences for evolution and the apparent elimination of a divine role in it by his theory that natural selection provided an automatic guiding principle. He delayed publication of his views until 1859 in part because he anticipated the vehement opposition to them by religious people.

In this chapter we examine the evidences for evolution taking place. The most relevant evidence comes from the examination of the remains of living things preserved in the strata of the earth. These remains can be as complete as frozen bodies of ice-age mammoths preserved in "cold storage" for thousands of years in the Arctic or as faint as trails and burrows left as imprints on ancient beaches petrified many millions of years ago. The earliest forms of life so far found were cellular forms similar to existing bacteria and cyanobacteria (once called blue-green algae). They are found in rocks approximately three billion years old. Their genetic material was not organized into chromosomes enclosed in a nuclear membrane (therefore they are called "procaryotes"). They multiplied by simple fission. About 1.5 billion years ago simple cellular forms appeared that can be classified as eucaryotes, i.e., having chromosomes enclosed in a nucleus and dividing by mitosis.

Life remained at this simple level for several hundred million years. Multicellular eucaryotes classified as animals made their appearance about 700 million years ago. Their presence is inferred from traces of their burrows. Apparently they were soft-bodied and wormlike. About 600 million years ago, more definite remains of soft-bodied animals are found. Some were like modern jelly-fishes. Not long after, the appearance of animals with some kind of skeleton can be inferred from scattered skeletal fragments (denticles, plates, etc.). With the beginning of the Cambrian period about 570 million years ago a profusion of hard-bodied animals appeared. They were all invertebrates. Some (e.g., trilobites) persisted for many millions of years, only to become extinct. Others (e.g., brachiopods and mollusks) gave rise to descendants that are still with us, relatively unchanged. Still others apparently gave rise to more complex descendants, most notably the chordates (animals with an axial supporting rod). The further evolution of the chordates has been particularly well traced in the fossil record. First came the jawless fishes in the Ordovician period about 500 million years ago. These gave rise successively in time to fishes with jaws, these to fishes with paddle-like fins, these to amphibians, these to reptiles. From reptiles diverged birds and mammals. In some cases the transitional forms are well-preserved. A classical example is the archaeopteryx, intermediate between reptiles and primitive birds.

The successive geological strata also record the progress of plant evolution. The first plants, simple unicellular algae, appeared about 1.5 billion years ago. These eventually gave rise to very simple vascular plants (psilophytes) about 400 million years ago. From these came club mosses, horse-tails, and ferns, all of which reproduce by spores. Primitive seed-bearing plants soon appeared and gave rise to the gymnosperms (with naked seeds). Only about 225 to 180 million years ago came the first angiosperms (with seeds enclosed in the ovule). These diversified immensely to give rise to the familiar and dominant flowering plant forms (trees, bushes, and herbs) of today. The picture of plant evolution as recorded in the rocks is not as clear as that of animal evolution, but still can be traced in broad outlines.

The evidence for evolution from the fossil record is strengthened and confirmed by data from many other sources.

One source of such evidence is provided by the data of comparative anatomy. For example, the forelimb of all vertebrates can be interpreted as modified from the condition in a primitive ancestor of one upper limb bone (humerus), two parallel lower limb bones (radius and ulna), and a hand with a number of carpal bones terminated by five metacarpals plus five digits. In some vertebrates as the primates (humans, etc.) the primitive condition was maintained essentially unchanged while in others it has been altered. Thus in birds the fourth and fifth digits are missing while the second and third form the main skeletal support for the primary flight feathers. The first digit is much reduced but supports feathers. In bats the first digit is free and of typical size, but the other four are greatly elongated and support the wing membrane. In modern horses only the third digit is retained with its distal phalanx capped by the hoof. The first and fifth digits are missing while the second and fourth are represented only by metacarpal vestiges (the "splints"). In these examples the elements of the forelimb have been altered as required to fit the particular vertebrate for the demands of its environment.

Another line of evidence comes from the geographical distribution of plants and animals. The present day geographical distribution is best explained by the view that the plants and animals have descended from ancestors evolving either where they are at present or from ancestors that evolved elsewhere but were able to reach their present sites because no barriers (e.g., mountain ranges, deserts, seas) prevented their migration. An example of the first situation are the armadillos of South America. Those closely resemble fossil armored mammals found in the rock strata of South America, and presumably evolved from them. This situation was already observed by Charles Darwin and was one of the evidences that convinced him that evolution had occurred. An example of the second situation, also observed by Charles Darwin, are the finches found on the Galapagos Islands. These most closely resemble species found on the mainland of nearby South America. The explanation is that some ancestral finches were blown over by winds from the mainland to the islands and there their descendants evolved into several species each adapted to a particular ecological niche available on the islands.

Some special cases which at first sight cannot be explained by the two origins of present day geographical distribution have been clarified by the now widely accepted concept of "continental drift." According to this concept, the continents are exposed portions of a number of great "plates" which divide up the earth's crust. These plates are separated by fracture zones in the oceans where new crust is produced by up-welling of subcrustal materials. The process causes the plates to move. Plates that were once in continuity are now far apart and others are colliding with each other. Thus South America, Africa, and India were in contact 200 million years ago and shared a similar fauna. The amphibians and reptiles inhabiting these regions at that time were almost identical as shown by their fossil remains. Why they were so similar was a puzzle, now solved by the new understanding provided by the concept of continental drift. Only since the drifting apart of the underlying plates have their fauna and flora diverged so that they are now quite different.

Another source of evidence for evolution comes from taxonomy, the study of the classification of plants and animals, based mainly on structural resemblances. Thus individuals that closely resemble each other and are fertile when crossed, are assigned to the same species. If they differ only in some respect usually minor such as color, but cannot be crossed, or, if crossed, have only sterile progeny, they are classified as separate species. However, because of their close resemblances, they are classified as members of a single genus. When one refers to an animal or plant in a scientific treatise, one gives the genus and species designations assigned to it. Thus the house cat is *Felis domesticus*. This convention was established by the Swedish botanist Carl Linnaeus (1707-1778) and is known as the binomial system of nomenclature. The names assigned are always in Latin or in Latinized versions to insure worldwide uniformity of nomenclature. Similar genera are grouped together into families, similar families into orders, similar orders into classes, similar classes into phyla. Finally similar phyla are grouped together into one or the other of the great Kingdoms (Animal, Plant, etc.). *The basis for the possibility of the classification of organisms into these groups according to their similarities in basic body plan and other characteristics is best explained scientifically by common descent with modifications, i.e., by evolution. The* more similar organisms are, it is argued, the more closely related by common descent they are.

Plants and animals obviously are very different in many important respects. Yet they must have had a common ancestor in the very remote past. This conclusion follows from the fact that they possess very basic characteristics in common, e.g., the bearers of heredity in both, the genes, are made up of deoxyribonucleic acid (DNA), their genetic code is the same, they both use the same isomeric forms of only 20 amino acids to build their proteins, they both use the compound adenosine triphosphate to store energy, they have similar processes of cell division, the fundamental laws of heredity for both are identical, and so forth.

Taxonomy relies for practical purposes mostly on how similar the structures (anatomy) of plants and animals are. The assumption is that the more alike these structures are, the more they reflect a common heredity and therefore the organisms with these similar characteristics should taxonomically be grouped together. However, we can now examine the actual genetic material, DNA, of different organisms for similarities and by inference common origins. The key idea here is that we can measure the degree of genetic relationship of two organisms by determining how similar the structure of their DNA's are. Organisms sharing the heredity of some fairly immediate ancestor will have very similar if not identical DNA. In proportion as organisms are more and more distantly related, the structures of their DNA's will differ.

The structure of DNA is made up of two anti-parallel strands. Each strand is a linear polymer of nucleotides. Each nucleotide consists of three subunits: deoxyribose (a 5-carbon sugar), one of 4 organic bases (the purines adenine and guanine, and the pyrimidines thymine and cytosine), and phosphate. The backbone of the strand is produced by bonding the sugar of one nucleotide with the phosphate of the next. The four bases joined to successive sugars in the backbone of one strand, called the coding strand, can be grouped into triplets, i.e., successions of three bases. A total of 64 combinations of three successive bases is possible and each combination has a coding function. Sixty-one of the triplets code for one of the 20 amino acids used by organisms to make up their proteins. Three of the triplets code for no amino acid and function as "stop signals" in the process of joining amino acids to form a protein. Since only 20 amino acids need to be coded for, several triplets often code for the same amino acid.

DNA's belonging to organisms of the same species and therefore sharing fairly close ancestors will have the same sequence of triplets, or, more generally the same sequence of bases on their coding and non-coding strands. If the organisms differ in their heredity, these sequences will differ and the degree of difference in sequences will be a measure of how much their heredity differs. How can one determine the identity or difference in base sequences of two organisms? Here a very important feature of the structure of DNA is critical. It is the fact that the two anti-parallel strands in one DNA molecule are bound together by so-called "hydrogen bonds" between the bases of the coding strand and the bases of the non-coding strand. This bonding is very specific in that adenine (A) in one strand at a particular position is bound only to thymine (T) in the other strand, and guanine (G) similarly only to cytosine (C). If the order of the bases in one strand is A T T A C G, then the order of the bases in the other strand at this region will be T A A T G C. The extent and strength of the binding of one strand of DNA to another is determined by how complementary the sequence of the bases in the one strand is to the other. This is the rationale for the following experiment.

It is possible, after fragmenting the very long DNA helices of two organisms into short segments of a few hundred nucleotides and then heating to about 100 degrees Centigrade to separate the members of one strand from the other, and then to allow them to rejoin by slowly lowering the temperature. If this is done with the DNA of one species, the complementary strands of similar DNA molecules will rejoin to restore essentially the original arrangement. If the disassociated strands of the DNA of two different species are allowed to recombine, the amount of recombination can vary from an amount essentially equal to that of each species separately to practically no recombination. Since the DNA makes up the gene complements of species and hence their heredity determinants, the amount of recombination measures the degree of identity of the heredity of the two species. In an experiment using DNA from man and DNA from the chimpanzee, one obtains over 98 percent recombination. This can only be possible if the gene sequences of man and chimpanzee are very similar if not nearly identical. This finding is one of the reasons why anthropologists believe that man is more closely related by evolutionary descent to the chimpanzee than to the other primates such as the gorilla. In another experiment using DNA again from man but this time DNA from the chicken, only 10 percent recombination is found. We can conclude that man and chicken have only about 10 percent of their genetic sequences similar and so share only a very remote evolutionary ancestor, perhaps among the reptiles, which as we infer from the fossil record gave rise to both birds and mammals many millions of years ago.

*The results of the studies using the DNA hybridization technique with respect to evolutionary relationships are in substantial agreement with the results of other studies using different approaches, e.g., those based on fossils and comparative anatomy.* Most recently the actual DNA nucleotide sequences of specific "homologous" genes are being compared in different species. The results of these studies under way will allow scientists to evaluate even better the evolutionary relationships between different species.

Another molecular approach to trace evolutionary relationships is to compare the amino acid sequences of proteins having similar structures and functions in organisms, so-called "homologous proteins." The idea here is that the more similar these sequences are, the more likely they reflect as their source a common ancestor. In these studies we are determining genetic similarities one step removed from the actual gene (DNA) sequences. This follows from the fact noted above that the sequence of amino acids in a protein is determined by the sequence of coding triplets in the DNA gene molecule.

To date, hundreds of proteins have been completely or partly sequenced, and each year many more are added to these. The sequences are stored in central data banks. Thus any new sequence can be rapidly compared with others in the banks for similarities. For an example of the light which comparison of the amino acid sequences of homologous proteins can throw on evolutionary relationships, we can take the protein cytochrome c. This protein plays an essential role in cellular respiration, so it is not surprising that its amino acid sequence has tolerated relatively few alterations over evolutionary time. The amino acid sequences of cytochrome c of many organisms ranging from man down to yeast have been determined. The resemblances are so great that in this case a statistical test to exclude origin of the similarities by chance is not really needed. We can be sure that all present day cytochrome c's go back to one ancestral form in the very remote past. *The amino acids present at similar relative positions in the cytochromes of the organisms studied are often identical. When they do differ, we note that the degree of difference almost always agrees with the evolutionary relationships of the organisms as inferred from other evidences such as from fossils or comparative anatomy.* Thus the cytochromes of man and the chimp are identical while the cytochrome of man differs from that of the Rhesus monkey by only one amino acid, but differs from that of the horse by eleven.

*As we conclude our review of the main evidences for evolution, the point should be emphasized that all these evidences have a cumulative effect, viz., the various pieces of evidence reinforce each other and all point to a common natural explanation in evolution. On a scientific level there is certainly no explanation that can seriously compete with the evolutionary explanation.* Thus it is not surprising that the vast majority of informed natural scientists accept the reality of evolution. Only a few fundamentalist scientists deny it and this ultimately for religious, not scientific reasons. We have seen that their appeal to the scriptural account of creation as contradicting evolution is ill-informed. Since there is no scriptural basis for denying evolution and the scientific evidence is compelling, there appears to be no basis for any conflict between natural science and Christian faith in this matter. Christian faith still affirms that the ultimate origin of the entire universe including the living creatures on earth is God, but grants that this origin was not by simple fiat but by the process of evolution. In other words, God created by setting in motion and sustaining the natural process of evolution.

Since the scientific evidence accumulated for the historical reality of evolution has been steadily increasing, it is not surprising that authorities in the Roman Catholic Church have passed from a very skeptical attitude to one of acceptance at least of its possibility. The Fathers of the Second Vatican Council (1963-1965) imply as much when they acknowledge in the section "Deep-Seated Changes" in the *Pastoral Constitution on the Church in the Modern World* (No. 5) that "the human race has passed from a rather static concept of reality to a more dynamic, evolutionary one." More clearly yet, Pope John Paul II in his catechetical instructions when discussing the creation of man concedes the possibility that man's body (but not his soul) was created by God by an evolutionary process. The Pope is not greatly concerned about whether animals below man evolved but at least implicitly admits its possibility in statements like this: "If the human body did evolve, God would have willed and foreseen every single gene mutation and natural selection process on the path from the very first, most simple animal species to the most complex animal and ultimately to the crowning glory of material creation: the human body."

In regard to evolution, however, a most important question remains to be examined: does the way, the mechanism by which evolution comes about as proposed and accepted by natural scientists exclude any role for God in the process? We examine this question in the next chapter.

## SUGGESTED READINGS

1. Ayala, Francis J. and J.A. Kiger, Jr., *Modern Genetics* (Menlo Park, CA: Benjamin/Cummings, 1980).

2. Ayala, Francis J., "The Theory of Evolution: Recent Successes and Challenges," pp. 59-90 in *Evolution and Creation*, Ernan McMullin, ed. (Notre Dame, IN: Notre Dame Press, 1985).

3. Bresch, Carsten, "Evolution and Creation Faith," *Theology Digest*, v. 34: pp. 139-144, 1987.

4. Flannery, Austin, O.P., Gen. ed., *Vatican Council II*, Para. 5, "Deep-Seated Changes," pp. 906-907 in *The Pastoral Constitution on the Church in the Modern World*, December 7, 1965 (Boston, MA: St. Paul Editions, 1988).

5. Gray, Jane and William Shear, "Early Life on Land," *American Scientist*, v. 80: pp. 444-456, 1992.

6. Hogan, Richard M. and John M. LeVoir, "God's Love: Creation," Ch. 2, esp. pp. 31-33 in *Faith for Today: Pope John Paul II's Catechetical Teachings* (New York, NY: Doubleday, 1988).

7. Li, Wen-Hsiung and Dan Grauer, *Fundamentals of Molecular*

*Evolution* (Sunderland, MA: Sinauer Associates, Inc., 1990).

8. Schopf, J. William, "Microfossils of the Early Archean Apex Chart: New Evidence of the Antiquity of Life," *Science*, v. 260: pp. 640-646, 1993.

# CHAPTER 9

# Darwin's Mechanism for Evolution: Natural Selection

arwin in his work *The Origin of Species* had in mind to accomplish two goals: the first was proving the reality of evolution for the origin of the world of life by marshalling a massive amount of evidence from the data of geographic distribution, comparative embryology and anatomy, and so forth, as known at his time. In the preceding chapter we went over some of the same lines of evidence and added new ones developed since Darwin's time. Darwin's second goal was his special and distinctive contribution, viz., to provide a natural mechanism for how evolution could take place: his theory of natural selection.

In searching for this mechanism, Darwin noted that species of animals and plants gave rise to many variations. He observed that animal and plant breeders by long-continued selection of some of these variations had produced domestic varieties of animals and plants breeding true for some desired characteristic. An example known to Darwin was how pigeon fanciers had produced numerous varieties of pigeons, such as tumblers, fan- tails, and so forth, by selecting from variants arising in flocks of the domesticated rock dove *Columba livia*. Darwin's quest for a parallel in nature for this artificial selection came to fruition from his reading of *An Essay on the Principle of Population* (1798; rev. ed. 1803) by Thomas Robert Malthus (1776-1834). Malthus concluded that the population of mankind increases in geometrical ratio — and hence faster — than the means of subsistence, which increases only in arithmetical ratio. Thus an intense competition for the means of livelihood ensues. Famine along with war and crime strike down the most wretched and poor. Thus the human population remains in a painful equilibrium with its sources of supply.

Reading this essay, Darwin at once saw how Malthus' concept could be applied to his problem of finding in nature a driving mechanism for evolution. Here is how he expressed his idea in *The Origin of Species* (6th ed., p. 128):

> If under changing conditions of life organic beings present individual difference in almost every part of their structure, and this cannot be disputed; if there be, owing to their geometrical ratio of increase, a severe struggle for life at some age, season, or year, and this certainly cannot be disputed; then considering the infinite complexity of the relations of all organic beings to each other and to their conditions of life, causing an infinite diversity in structure, constitution, and habits, to be advantageous to them, it would be a most extraordinary fact if no variations ever occurred useful to each being's welfare, in the same manner as so many variations have occurred useful to man. But if variations useful to any organic being ever do occur, assuredly individuals thus characterized will have the best chance of being preserved in the struggle for life; and from the strong principle of inheritance, these will tend to produce offspring similarly characterized. This principle of preservation, of the *survival of the fittest* [italics added], I have called Natural Selection. It leads to the improvement of

each creature in relation to the organic and inorganic conditions of life; and consequently, in most cases, to what must be regarded as an advance in organization.

Unfortunately Darwin was seduced by the clever ring of the phrase "survival of the fittest" to adopt this expression as equivalent to his "natural selection." Thus countless readers of Darwin have been led to think that mere survival while others perish is the important aspect of natural selection. Darwin however explicitly stated that he took the struggle for existence in a very metaphorical sense and that the important element in this process was success in leaving progeny. A further problem was created by the word "fittest" in the expression "survival of the fittest." Fittest to many has meant the strongest or the most clever or the best morally. However, to repeat, to Darwin the fittest were those who were most successful in leaving progeny to the succeeding generation. To man's eye these organisms may be quite unattractive specimens but it is their heredity that will dominate their species eventually.

To sum up, then, Darwin's idea of natural selection had three key elements: first, in nature individuals of the same species vary among themselves; second, these variations are partly at least determined by heredity; third, when the possessors of these variations leave progeny to the next generation, those contributing the most progeny will be relatively the most successful in leaving their characteristics to succeeding generations. In the long run, those parents leaving the most progeny will do so because they possess characteristics best fitting them to survive and reproduce in their particular environment. But changing environments will demand changes in the adaptations of species living in these environments. Eventually the members of a species may be altered so much that they can be rightly designated as forming a new species. If the members of what originally was one species, became adapted to two or more different environments, we could eventually have a separation into two or more species.

Some biologists have thought that natural selection acts only to eliminate ill-adapted organisms. They have assigned to it a merely negative and passive role, much as though it were a sieve which holds back and rejects the misfits. Such a concept of natural selection can give no satisfactory explanation for the origin of the adaptations themselves. Many of these, as the eye, are quite complex and must involve the coordinated interactions of many genes. If natural selection merely rejects the ill-adapted, then "chance" must be appealed to for the origin of adaptations. But the probability that such a favorable combination of gene mutations will occur at random is extremely small. If evolution depended on this source of adaptation alone, geological time would not be sufficient to allow all of them to occur. However, a more sophisticated understanding of the operation of natural selection gives it a positive and even creative role in the origin of adaptations. Gene mutations that by themselves may be harmful but which are beneficial in company with others can be retained in the gene pool if recessive. If they are initially dominant, modifiers will be accumulated by natural selection that will make them recessive and thus allow them to be retained in the gene pool. Such temporarily harmful genes can be positively favored and increase in frequency when they become associated with genes with which they favorably interact. Of course, any mutation that by itself confers even a slight degree of better adaptation will be favored and grow in frequency in the gene pool. In this view of natural selection, the development of a complex adaptation is a very gradual affair and goes through many less perfect stages, each of which is an improvement on previous stages. The gene combinations for each stage are not broken up completely in proceeding to a new stage, but provide the basis for the new combinations involved.

The actual course of evolution as seen in the fossil record

appears to be guided by two factors: an available environmental opportunity and the capability of some organism to exploit it. Sometimes an environmental opportunity was available but no organism at the time had the adaptations needed to exploit it. For example, for millions of years in the Mesozoic era, swarms of insects were aloft in the atmosphere but no predators were there to feed on them. Eventually a tree-hopping small dinosaur in a series of stages developed the numerous adaptations needed for successful flight, and became a mainly diurnal predator on the insect bounty. Much later a small mammal followed suit, and bats joined the birds in the air and exploited the atmospheric opportunity left open after sunset by birds. Contemplating the past evolutionary history of life, scientists like Richard Dawkins see no goal imposed by some divine being on its course. Evolution seems to have been essentially guided by environmental opportunity. If the environment did not change, organisms already adapted to it could not change. Several decades ago the scientific public was astounded by the discovery of living coelacanth fishes in the seas off the Madagascar coast of Africa. Until these living representatives (named *Latimeria*) were found, the coelocanths (a form of very ancient lobe-fin fishes so-called because their fins were supported by limb-like stalks) were known only as fossils recovered in strata 60 million years old. Apparently the living coelocanths survived over this immense stretch of time unchanged because the habitat to which they were adapted did not change. In very many other cases organisms not or ill-adapted to new environmental demands died out. The geological strata are full of examples, e.g., the dinosaurs. In some cases organisms with some features pre-adapting them to the new conditions survived. Among the survivors, the variants arising over time with improvements in their adaptations gradually dominated the population. If the environment changed over time in one constant direction, the changes of organisms adapting to the changing environment would necessarily also exhibit a corresponding directional change. This is well shown by the gradual changes in teeth, feet, and other organs observed in the evolution of the horse adapting it to the changes from forest to grass plain conditions in Western North America.

What can the believer in a personal God and Divine Providence for the world answer to the assertions of scientists like Dawkins that the opportunistic way in which evolution actually occurred excludes any idea that its course was planned to achieve any goal, including one set by God? Obviously the believer cannot adopt the view of the Deists who say that God created the world with its forces and laws and then played no further role in its history. He remembers the words of Christ who said that not even a sparrow falls to the ground without the consent of His Father.

Light on how God acts in evolution comes from reflecting on how He acts in the world of rational creatures, human beings. God has given them free will: the ability to make free choices between alternative ways of acting, knowing that their actions will have consequences. This allows them to choose the good instead of the bad. But free-will also allows humans to choose the bad instead of the good. Thus God permits sin, moral evil, to enter the world, not for its own sake, but as a concomitant of the gift of free will.

What light can these considerations shed on the course of evolution? Just as God has not imposed a rigid necessary way of acting on humans without free will, so God has allowed the equivalent of freedom in how natural forces act in the world of life. The general good result is that we see a world of living things adapted in various ways to their environments. We see also that, at least in some lineages, progress up the scale of life has been achieved. This progress is most conspicuous in the line that led to the emergence of humans. But the general trend to adaptation to environmental possibilities has also included widespread parasitism. Parasitism must be considered a successful way of life for organisms whose environment came to include the bodies of other organisms. As repulsive as they appear to us, for example, the tapeworms are well adapted to life in the intestines of their hosts.

The Christian believer can turn the argument of agnostic natural scientists against their conclusion that no God could be involved in the course of evolution because it included reliance on the random occurrence of favorable mutations to provide the basis for adaptations. Agnostics tend to conceive God as a totalitarian monarch who cannot allow any spontaneity, any unpredictability to the events in His plan for evolution. The Christian believer, on the other hand, can point to the varied adaptations to their environments achieved by organisms on the basis of random genetic changes selected by their suitability for meeting environmental demands and conclude that God used a method which, despite its reliance on opportunism, did achieve survival and even progress up the scale of life.

The Christian believer sees God as ever present and working in creation. But God is not one cause along with other causes in the process of evolution. To the Christian believer, God is the ultimate *ground* conferring and maintaining the existence of all beings. He is also the *ground* for all their activities. Thus the entire course of evolution depended ultimately on God for its initiation and progress. This role of God must be understood correctly. The Creator's role does not exclude the roles of secondary causes in evolution, such as chance mutations and natural selection. It does mean that these secondary causes could not exist and achieve the results of their activities without God's concurrence. Since natural science is concerned only with the existence and activities of these secondary observable causes, the role of God is opaque to it. Science can make no statement about it. Only philosophy and theology can discover the role of God in evolution. In effect, only the Christian believer has access to this aspect of phenomena including here especially evolution.

The point to make here is that there need be no opposition between Christian faith and natural science in understanding the way evolution proceeded. Natural science, despite the assertions of some scientists, cannot exclude the role of God as the ultimate explanation of evolution and the way it proceeded. In turn Christian faith should not exclude the role of natural processes including opportunism in the way God brought about evolution and its results. Natural science of itself is powerless to discover any plan or purpose behind evolution. Only Christian faith can discover the plan and purpose of God in bringing about evolution: namely, to bring into existence a rational being who could know, love, and serve God, and thus eventually attain complete fulfillment and happiness with his Creator.

In concluding this chapter, I freely confess that I have not completely resolved the fundamental problem here, which is how to reconcile two truths. The first, held by every Christian believer, is that God as the Omniscient and Omnipotent Supreme Being has determined from all eternity whatever happens in this world so that it fulfills the Creator's plan. The other, held by most natural scientists, is that the evolution of life characterized by opportunism seems to reflect no plan but a reliance on the concurrence of apparently chance mutations with favorable environments to produce unpredictable results, results which, nonetheless, are not beyond the realm of possibility. I have tried to reconcile these two truths by showing that they do not contradict each other because they express truths on different levels: the first on the level of ultimate primary causality, the second on the level of proximate secondary causality.

The solution of this problem will not surprise Christian believers who have struggled with a very similar problem: how to reconcile these two truths: first, humans are truly free to choose between various courses of action, to choose the good or the bad; and second, God as the Omniscient and Omnipotent Supreme Being has from all eternity foreseen and determined these choices in some way. I believe that no completely satisfactory solution for *this* problem has ever been achieved, despite numerous attempts by great thinkers. One such attempt, by Thomas Aquinas, states that God as the First Cause moves free agents as secondary causes to actions that for them are free and independent.

After conceiving the proposal that God uses what to us are chance events to bring about His plan for evolution, I have found that Arthur R. Peacocke has made a similar proposal. I refer the reader to two of his works in the list of Suggested Readings appended to this chapter.

## SUGGESTED READINGS

1. Darwin, Charles, *The Origin of Species* (New York, NY: The New American Library of World Literature: Mentor Edition, 1958).

2. Dawkins, Richard, *The Blind Watchmaker: Why the Evidence of Evolution Reveals a Universe without Design* (New York, NY: W.W. Norton & Co., Inc., 1988).

3. Monod, Jacques, *Chance and Necessity: An Essay on the Natural Philosophy of Modern Biology*, tr. Austryn Wainhouse (New York, NY: Alfred A. Knopf, Inc., 1971).

4. Peacocke, Arthur R., *Creation and the World of Science* (Oxford: Clarendon Press, 1979).

5. Peacocke, Arthur R., *Intimations of Reality* (Notre Dame, IN: University of Notre Dame Press, 1984).

CHAPTER 10

# The Evolution of Man

W hatever else human beings are, they are a part of the world of nature. Each human being begins as one cell, the zygote, formed by the union of male sperm and female egg. The zygote divides again and again and forms a solid ball of many cells (the morula). As it passes down the oviduct of the female, the morula hollows out and forms the blastocyst. On arrival in the uterus, part of the blastocyst cooperates with cells of the maternal uterus and forms the placenta. Another part gives rise to the embryo proper, joined to the life-sustaining placenta by the umbilical cord. The cells of the embryo rapidly multiply and differentiate to form specialized tissues and organs. By the third month the tiny creature only about 28 mm. long is recognizably human. Succeeding months are spent in more growth and continued development. At birth nine months later the human infant is still entirely dependent on its mother's care for survival. It will be years before it is an adult of the species, years spent in learning to walk, to speak, to assimilate human culture, and to be able to reproduce its own kind.

As an animal, there seems to be nothing completely unique about humans. Their cells are made up of the same chemical elements organized into similar molecules of nucleic acids, proteins, fats, and so forth, as in other animals. The nuclei of human cells contain the same heredity-bearing molecules as in other animals (DNA). The DNA combined with proteins is organized into sets of chromosomes as in other animals. Thus the laws of heredity transmission are the same in humans as in other animals. The chromosomal basis of sex determination in humans is the XY mechanism shared by many animals. A human being is a fairly typical vertebrate animal. More specifically, a human is a mammal. Thus human anatomy, embryology, and physiology are typical of any mammal. And that is why the pre-med student can begin his study of human anatomy by first familiarizing himself with the anatomy of the cat (its bones, muscles, internal organs). In his or her study of embryology, the medical student may study the development of the pig. Actually the embryology of the mouse would be as useful.

Among the mammals, the most obvious resemblances to humans have always been found in the great apes (gorilla, chimpanzee, orangutan). These are classified in the family *Pongidae* while humans are the sole member of the family *Hominidae*. Both families are joined in the superfamily *Hominoidea*. Present opinion among primatologists is that all hominoids share a common ancestor about 18 to 22 million years ago. How and when the various hominoids split off is in dispute. One opinion is that the orangutans first split off the family tree 13 to 16 million years ago, leaving a common ancestor for the gorilla, chimp, and human. Still later, about 8 to 10 million years ago, the gorilla line split off, again leaving a common ancestor for the chimp and human. Then chimps and humans separated and began to evolve on divergent paths about 6 to 8 million years ago. Thus the closest living relative to man is the chimp.

There are various pieces of evidence which support the human's close relationship to the chimp. Thus, specialized chromosome staining techniques that reveal the pattern of banding show that the chromosomes of human and chimp possess the same series of bands with some different arrangements. One difference is that in the human, two chromosomes that are separate in the chimp have been joined into the #2 human chromosome. As a result the chimp's haploid chromosome number of 24 became reduced to 23 in the human. The other differences involve small pericentric inversions in human chromosomes #1 and #18. Since the bands of the chromosomes have a close relationship to gene loci, it appears that humans and chimps are very similar genetically. The differences in banding between the chromosomes of man and those of the gorilla or orangutan are considerably greater than between humans and chimps. Earlier we noted that DNA hybridization studies also showed that human and chimp are very much alike in the sequence of DNA bases. Since the DNA is the genetic material, this line of evidence also argues for the close genetic similarity of humans and chimps. Recent studies in which long stretches of DNA base pairs have been actually sequenced confirm this conclusion. In these studies a sequence of over 10,000 base pairs in the beta-globin region in humans, chimps, gorillas, and orangutans has been analyzed. While not identical, non-coding base sequences of humans and chimps differ only in 1.6 percent whereas the same sequences in chimps and gorillas differ in 2.1 percent.

Despite all the cytological and molecular evidence closely linking humans and chimps, some anthropologists who put strong weight on comparative anatomy think that chimp and gorilla are closely related because both share the anatomical specializations fitting them for "knuckle-walking," i.e., walking bent over with some weight supported on the knuckles of the forelimbs. Humans do not have these anatomical specializations. Thus these anthropologists believe that when gorillas, chimps, and humans diverged from a common ancestor, one line led to gorilla and chimp, both with knuckle-walking, and the other to humans. As far as we are concerned, the point is of no critical importance, since in any case all agree that humans evolved from some ape-like ancestor.

*What then is the evidence for evolution of humans from a subhuman ancestor? The data from anatomy, embryology, physiology, cytology, and molecular biology all support the concept that humans like any other animal evolved. One might say that if despite all these evidences humans did not evolve from some animal ancestor, then no animal evolved and all are specially created. No scientist today could accept such a conclusion.*

As we saw in the chapter on the evidence for evolution of life in general, the most telling evidence for the evolution of humans comes from the historical record as preserved in the earth's strata. In Darwin's time, the fossil record for the early ancestors of humans was almost completely blank. In 1848 parts of a skull with thick bones, very prominent eyebrow ridges, and massive jaws were found at Gibraltar. These remains attracted little attention but in 1856 a similar skull cap plus some ribs and limb bones were found in the Neander valley of Germany. The being that left these remains was named *Homo neanderthalensis* and was regarded as a progenitor of modern man. From associated animal remains (bones of mammoths, woolly rhinoceroses, etc.) and other lines of evidence, Neanderthal man is now dated back to about 300,000 years ago and disappeared from the fossil record as such about 35,000 years ago. Neanderthal man was definitely human. His brain was even larger than modern man (average 1450 cc. vs. 1350 cc.). Neanderthal man made crude stone tools and buried his dead. Since the first find, many other more or less complete skeletons of Neanderthal man have been found scattered over Europe, Asia, the Near East, and Africa.

In 1868 during the construction of a railroad in the Dordogne region of France, human skeletal remains were found buried in the rear of a cave called Cro-Magnon. These fossils were associated with stone, bone, and antler tools much better made than those found with Neanderthal remains. Since the skulls though ancient were identical with those of modern humans — short with thin bone walls and high vaults, large cranial capacity (one adult's capacity was 1590 cc., well above the mean for modern man, which is 1350 cc.), very moderate brow ridges, small jaws and teeth, and definite chins — no great excitement was aroused by their discovery. These finds and numerous subsequent ones in Europe have been ascribed to Cro-Magnon man after the name of the French cave in which they were first found. They are dated to 35,000 years before the present. Associated with Cro-Magnon man we find in Europe a remarkable outburst of art and technology. All are familiar with the beautiful realistic paintings of animals on the walls of caves in Altamira, Spain and Lascaux, France. On the walls are also found engravings and bas-relief sculptures. The stone tools were expertly worked and were of many kinds (engravers, scrapers, chisels, and saws). The bow-and-arrow, spear thrower and harpoon were invented. Bone, antler, ivory, and wood were used to make tools, tent poles, clothes fasteners, necklaces, amulets, and statuettes.

The next important discovery occurred in central Java. There in 1891 the Dutch army surgeon Eugène Dubois (1858-1940) found a skull cap, a jaw fragment, and a femur. The skull cap had heavy eyebrow ridges. In this it was apelike but surpassed all apes in its brain size, calculated as 900 cc. From the form of the femur, Dubois deduced that it walked upright. Dubois thought that he had found the "missing link" between apes and humans and therefore named his find *Pithecanthropus erectus*, the erect ape-man. In 1929 Davison Black found in a cave near Zhoukoudian (Chou-k'ou-tien) in China a nearly complete skull similar to *Pithecanthropus* which he named *Sinanthropus pekinensis*. Both in Java and in China, many more skulls, jaws, and other bones were found in subsequent years. Detailed analysis has shown that all these remains found in Java, China, and later on in Africa and Europe belong to only one human type now known as *Homo erectus*. His skull retained ape-like features (retreating forehead, heavy eyebrow ridges, massive jaws projecting somewhat, no chin, and large teeth). He differed from apes in the much larger brain (average 1975 cc. vs. 500 cc. in the gorilla), teeth similar to modern human's in specific characteristics, and erect posture. He made crude tools of chipped stone and bone, and used fire to cook. He lived from about 1.6 million to 300,000 years ago.

All along the common view of anthropologists was that humans first evolved a brain with human capabilities and only later assumed erect posture. This view had to be discarded when a new series of fossils was discovered. In 1924 Raymond Dart found in a cave in South Africa a child's skull combining a mixture of ape and human features. He called it *Australopithecus*, the southern ape. Later on skulls of adults were found. The brain size was larger than in modern chimps (average 500 cc. vs. 375 cc.) but still well below that of modern humans (average 1350 cc.). The skull has some ape-like features (eyebrow ridges, protruding jaws) but not as pronounced as in the chimp. A chin was lacking. The teeth in general were quite human; the canines were large but much smaller than in the chimp. The canines, premolars, and molars were not arranged in parallel rows as in all apes, but diverged at the back as in modern man. The occipital condyles (the rounded prominences at the end of the lower back part of the skull) by which the skull articulates with the spinal column were under the ventral (front) surface of the skull instead of at its end. This position of the condyles argues for an erect posture for *Australopithecus*. This view is confirmed by the shape of the pelvis. This is not long and narrow as in the apes, but shallow and basin-like as in modern humans.

There were at least two kinds of *Australopithecus*: one was a slender "gracile" form, the other a more robust form. *Australopithecus*, the earliest animal believed to be on the evolutionary path to modern man, walked upright with hands free for other uses than for locomotion. Whether these hands were used to make tools is not clear. It is probable that like the modern chimp, *Australopithecus* used sticks and stones to procure food and to defend itself.

82

*Australopithecus* can be fairly accurately dated from the fossil-bearing strata as existing approximately 5 to 1 million years ago.

In the 1930's, in Israel in the Qafzeh cave skeletal remains of modern *Homo sapiens* were uncovered. These created no great interest at the time because they were dated at about 45,000 years before the present, thus only slightly older than the Cro-Magnon *Homo sapiens* of Europe. But recently (1988) the Qafzeh remains have been dated by a new technique (thermolumines-cence) as being 92,000 years old. The significance of this new date is that it makes modern man contemporaneous with Nean-derthal man. Thus it is very improbable that Neanderthal man evolved into modern *Homo sapiens*. It also moves the evolution of modern man back well more than 100,000 years before the present. The tool technology of these early modern *Homo sapiens* was relatively primitive when compared to that of Cro-Magnon man. We can conclude from this that the state of tool technology can lag behind the development of the brain.

In 1973 Richard Leakey found on the shores of Lake Turkana in Kenya, Africa, the skeletal remains of a hominid with a significantly larger brain than in *Australopithecus robustus*, whose remains were also found in the same deposits. This brain was estimated in an adult as being 775 cc. in volume. Found along with skeletal remains were crude stone tools. These were merely stone pebbles chipped at one end to make crude scrapers and choppers. Leakey called the new find *Homo habilis* because of its association with tools. *Homo habilis* probably arose a little more than 2 million years ago. Since he was contemporaneous with *Australopithecus robustus*, he is thought to have evolved from the other form of *Australopithecus*, the gracile *Australopithecus afarensis*.

In the preceding overview, we followed the chronological order of time of discovery and have placed emphasis on the discovery of fossil remains that appear to represent significant steps in the evolutionary ascent to modern man. At present, most would find acceptable these successive stages: *Australopithecus*

83

*afarensis, Homo habilis, Homo erectus, Homo sapiens*. No attempt was made to present a complete and detailed account of all the fossil evidence available. The works cited in the Suggested Readings after this chapter may be consulted for more details.

At this point, it may be useful to state that, although the fact of evolution is scientifically accepted as underlying modern biology, theories that concern themselves with the processes of evolution continue to be debated and refined. Much of this work involves highly sophisticated mathematical studies, as required by the complex interactions of the various elements which play a part in evolution: gene mutations, population genetics, ecological changes over a long period of time, and so forth. Because understanding of the actual evolutionary events that took place over earth's long history depends largely on interpretations of an incomplete fossil record, much latitude remains for differences in such interpretations.

One of the issues that is currently being debated among theorists derives from a notable fact observed in the fossil record. That is, when a new species appears in the record it usually does so abruptly and then apparently remains stable for as long as the record of that species lasts. The fossils do not seem to exhibit the slow and gradual changes that might be expected according to the modern hypotheses. For this reason, a number of evolutionists — most notably Stephen Jay Gould (1941- ) of Harvard University and Niles Eldredge (1943- ) of the American Museum of Natural History — have proposed a variant concept of "punctuated equilibria" for the evolution of species. According to this concept, species do in fact tend to remain stable for long periods of time (stasis) and then to change relatively abruptly — or rather, to be replaced suddenly by newer and more successful forms. These sudden changes are the "punctuations" in the state of equilibrium that give this concept its name.

The first individuals accepted by all as in the path of human evolution are the Australopithecines, specifically the gracile form *Australopithecus afarensis.* These were still more ape-like than human. Their forearm bones were relatively long in relation to their legs as in modern apes, which suggests that they retained the ability to climb trees. Their main claim to be pre-human are their brains (about 450 cc. in volume), larger than in apes, and their ability to walk upright. Anthropologists dispute whether they used artificial tools. Recently (1988) Randall L. Susman, from a study of hand bones attributed to a robust *Australopithecus* (*"Paranthropus"*), found evidence from their morphology that they were adapted for precision grasping and therefore for tool-making. The Australopithecines lived from 5 to about 1 million years ago.

Next comes *Homo habilis.* Besides an increase in brain size (in an adult about 775 cc.) he made stone tools. These were stones provided by percussion with edges suitable for use as crude cutting and scraping tools. *Homo habilis* probably lived from about 2.5 to about 1 million years ago and was contemporary with some form of *Australopithecus.*

*Homo erectus* made great improvements on the stone tools of *Homo habilis.* Besides making large choppers and hand-axes, *Homo erectus* made small tools such as various scrapers, blades, borers, and engravers. These small tools show much more skill in chipping than the pebble tools of *Homo habilis. Homo erectus* was a hunter of big game (elephants, rhinoceroses, horses, deer, and wild cattle) and used fire to prepare his food. He lived from about 1.6 million to 300,000 years ago. Earliest forms are estimated to have an average brain size of 940 cc. while later forms averaged 1000 cc. For the species as a whole, the range was 775 to 1300 cc.

*Homo neanderthalensis,* now often classified as a subspecies of *Homo sapiens* and named *Homo sapiens neanderthalensis,* was undoubt-edly human. He improved on the stone tools of *Homo erectus* by striking flakes off the surface of a suitable rock. These flakes were further worked by chipping to form a great variety of tools (borers, engravers, scrapers, knives, saws, etc.). The rock from which the flakes were removed served as a hand axe. *Homo neanderthalensis* was also a hunter of big game (reindeer, woolly rhinoceroses, mammoths) and was able to reside in caves by driving out and killing the cave bears. There is evidence that the Neanderthals had some kind of ritual involving the severed heads of cave bears. He also believed in a hereafter as shown, for example, by the burial of a youth carefully laid to rest on his right side with his head resting on his right forearm and a hand-axe laid by him. Charred wild cattle bones in the grave lead to the inference that the youth was provisioned for life after death. Neanderthal man lived from about 300,000 to 35,000 years ago and co-existed with modern *Homo sapiens* in the latter part of this time. At present most anthropologists think that Neanderthal man did not give rise to modern man. Why then did he disappear? Perhaps he was unable to compete successfully with fully modern man because he was less adept at hunting. Certainly his tool technology was very inferior to that of modern man. It is possible that he contributed genes to modern man by cross-breeding with him.

With the disappearance of the Neanderthals from the scene, the human population was dominated by *Homo sapiens*. The Cro-Magnon people, as we have seen, exhibited a great stride forward in culture. They made stone tools by striking blades off a core. These blades were further chipped into all manner of fine-worked tools. They also used bone, antler, and ivory for many kinds of uses including art objects (statuettes of the human female, for example). They did polychrome paintings, usually of the animals they hunted, on the walls of caves. Perhaps because the game was depleted by excessive hunting pressure, *Homo sapiens* later began to domesticate cattle, sheep, goats, pigs, and dogs. They also grew wild wheat, barley, peas, and lentils in fields by their villages. With this agricultural revolution humans no longer needed to hunt to survive. The subsequent story of humans' rapidly evolving culture need not concern us here. From this time on, human evolution is largely cultural evolution.

To sum up then, there is excellent evidence especially from fossil remains that humans evolved from ape-like ancestors. Most important in this evolution was a remarkable increase in brain volume. This allowed humans to make increasingly sophisticated tools until finally with their aid they dominated life on planet earth.

The problems raised by human evolution for a Christian believer will be discussed in the concluding sections of the next chapter.

## SUGGESTED READINGS

1. Gibbons, Ann, "Our Chimp Cousins Get That Much Closer," *Science*, v. 250: p. 376, 1990.

2. Lewin, Roger, "DNA Reveals Surprises in Human Family Tree," *Science*, v. 226: pp. 1179-1182, 1984.

3. Lewin, Roger, "Modern Human Origins Under Close Scrutiny," *Science*, v. 239: pp. 1240-1241, 1988.

4. Miyamoto, Michael M., Jerry L. Slighton and Morris Goodman, "Phylogenetic Relations of Human and African Apes from DNA Sequences in the psi-eta-Globin Region," *Science*, v. 238: pp. 369-372, 1987.

5. Putnam, John J., "The Search for Modern Humans," *National Geographic*, v. 174: pp. 438-477, 1988.

6. Rigaud, Jean-Philippe, "Treasures of Lascaux Cave," *National Geographic*, v. 174: pp. 482-499, 1988.

7. Stebbins, G. Ledyard, *Darwin to DNA, Molecules to Humanity* (San Francisco, CA: W.M. Freeman, 1982).

8. Stringer, Christopher B., "The Emergence of Modern Humans," *Scientific American*, v. 263: pp. 98-104, 1990.

9. Susman, Randall L., "Hand of *Paranthropus robustus* from Member 1, Swartkrans: Fossil Evidence for Tool Behavior," *Science*, v. 240: pp. 781-783, 1988.

10. Tullar, Richard M., *The Human Species: Its Nature, Evolution, and Ecology* (New York, NY: McGraw-Hill, 1977).

11. Yunis, Jorge Y. and Om Prakash, "The Origin of Man: A Chromosomal Pictorial Legacy," *Science*, v. 215: pp. 1525-1529, 1982.

CHAPTER 11

# The Uniqueness of Humans

If humans evolved like all other animals, what is unique about them? Especially, how do they differ from the chimpanzees, their closest living relatives? If we concentrate on human physical powers, many animals including the chimp are superior in brute strength. However there is one physical aspect in which humans excel all other animals: manual dexterity. When we examine the human brain, we see the neurological basis for this exceptional manual dexterity. The areas in the brain's cortex involved in the control of the human hand (especially the thumb) are tremendously enlarged when compared to the similar areas in the brain of a chimp. True, chimps can bring their thumb in contact with the tips of their other fingers and so have some manual dexterity. Also chimps have been observed in the wild making simple tools. Thus for example they prune twigs to probe for ants and termites. These are inserted into the openings in the nests and on withdrawal the insects clinging to them are eaten. If the end of the twig becomes bent, the chimp uses the other end or breaks off the bent end. Why chimps have stayed on a low level of tool use and have not progressed like humans in tool technology is partly explained by the small amount of their brain's cortex available for use in manual dexterity.

Chimps are social animals and communicate with each other by vocalizations, gestures, facial expressions, and bodily postures. Jane Goodall (1934- ), who spent years observing chimps in the wild, has described at least 23 different vocalizations used by them to express their feelings when angry, excited, enjoying food, startled, greeting other chimps, and so forth. They also employ a variety of gestures and bodily postures to communicate, some reminiscent of human behavior in similar circumstances. Thus they kiss to show affection. An adult male may greet an infant with a pat on the back. Chimps are thus able to express feelings to each other. But do they have thoughts (abstract concepts) which they express to each other?

Since we can never enter into the "mind" of a chimp directly any more than we can do this in the case of a fellow human being, we look for expressions of thought. Practically this means that we must see if chimps can invent and use a symbolic language. We have no evidence for this for wild chimps. People have made great efforts to teach chimps to speak but with no success. This may be impossible because the vocal apparatus of the chimp (larynx, tongue, etc.) may be unable to make human sounds. Therefore other approaches to see whether chimps can communicate symbolically have been taken. In one of these, B.T. and R.A. Gardner taught a year-old female chimp called Washoe the American Sign Language. This involves a formal set of gestures that symbolize various concepts. By age 7, Washoe had a "vocabulary" of 175 words. The investigators thought she showed some originality and understanding of the use of the language. Ann and David Premack taught another young female chimp Sarah to associate variously shaped and colored pieces of plastic with specific meanings. Sarah eventually had a "vocabulary" of about 130 words, which she used correctly about 80 percent of the time. In a third case, D.M. Rumbaugh and collaborators taught a young female chimp Lana to read and construct sentences using a computer. She operated a keyboard with 50 keys, each with different geometric shapes standing for a word. After six months Lana could use the computer to ask for food, drink, toys, music, and so forth. She also obeyed various instructions projected on the display panel.

These experiments seemed to show that chimps can be taught to *use* a symbolic language, but did they prove that chimps have the ability to make sentences by themselves without coaching by the experimenters? The experimenters thought that they had detected in their subjects some rudimentary ability to use linguistic rules to formulate sentences of their own. These experiments published between 1971 and 1973 were subjected in 1979 to devastating criticism by Herbert Terrace, a Columbia University psychologist. He pointed out major methodological flaws in the design of the experiments and showed that the chimps were merely imitating their human mentors and not really inventing sentences. No independent language ability was demonstrated by the experiments. For a time Terrace's criticisms deterred investigators from attacking the problem of chimp language ability, but not for long. Among those doing better controlled experiments are the Rumbaughs. The previous experiments performed by them and others were done with the common chimp species *Pan troglodytes*. This time the Rumbaughs used as their subject, Kanzi, a male pygmy chimp of the species *Pan paniscus*. Pigmy chimps are thought to more closely resemble humans in their behavior than common chimps. The Rumbaughs believe that Kanzi showed some capacity to invent new protogrammatical rules when communicating. These new results have received both favorable and unfavorable receptions from linguistic experts. One of the severest critics is the well-known MIT linguist Noam Chomsky who says that it is incredible that chimps have linguistic ability highly advantageous for their survival but use it only when taught by researchers.

If we grant that chimps do have some capacity to acquire a language, it is extremely rudimentary and vastly inferior to the facility with which a human youngster learns his or her native language. When we inspect the chimp brain for the cortical areas which in humans are concerned with memory, foresight, and language we obtain scant results. Most of the chimp's cortical areas are involved in sensory and motor functions. So one of the major differences between man and other animals including the chimps is the ability to invent and use a language based on arbitrary symbols to communicate.

Another difference between man and other animals is man's consciousness of self. A chimp was said to recognize her image in a mirror. If so, this could be an elementary form of self-consciousness. Humans can reflect on their knowledge and distinguish between various degrees of certitude. This ability has been expressed as "Only man knows that he knows." Humans can reflect on their origin and especially on their destiny. Humans are the only animals who are aware that they will die. Humans are also the only animals who speculate on their status after death: whether there is life for them after death. Related to this human characteristic is the fact that only humans have some form of religion: a concept of superior beings and efforts to communicate with them.

Humans differ from other animals also in their awareness of time. Humans are interested in what happened in the past and write histories. They also speculate about the future, what it has in store for them. They prepare calendars and predict eclipses. While the behavior of some animals is rigidly programmed (for instance, the building of a nest by a robin), other animals can learn to some extent from past experience and modify their behavior accordingly. The behavior of some animals prepares them for future contingencies. Thus a squirrel stores up nuts in the fall which will supply it in the winter, and many birds migrate between north and south and thus avoid the rigors of winter. But there is no need to postulate an awareness of the past or future to explain these actions, as if they were the result of reflection and planning. These actions contribute to the survival of the animals and have been made part of their heredity by natural selection.

Another difference between humans and other animals is that humans have a conscious appreciation of the beautiful. It is true that, for instance, the bower birds of New Zealand and Australia adorn their bowers with pretty flowers, stones, and pieces of glass. One of these birds is known to exchange fresh flowers for wilted ones from time to time. But the appreciation of beauty shown by animals is strictly limited and has not progressed further. Humans cultivate the arts of painting, sculpture, music, and architecture and have produced superb works of art. They have speculated on what constitutes the beautiful. A chimp can be taught to daub various colored paints on a canvas, but the results can be called "artistic" only by debasing the concept.

Humans are also remarkable for their originality. They find novel solutions to problems. At first these contrivances were very simple. Recall man's slow progress in perfecting stone implements for many thousands of years, then the rapid progress achieved by modern man in technology. Inventions followed in rapid succession: the time from the invention of the wheel to that of the jet plane for transportation is only a few thousand years. The progress in mathematics is instructive. First humans learned to count and invented a system of numbering. Then they used these to construct measures of time, weight, and distance. The need to construct irrigation ditches and to measure land areas led to geometry in Babylon and Egypt. Algebra was invented by the same peoples to solve practical problems such as the number of bricks needed to construct a building ramp of given dimensions. Calculus came later with Leibnitz and Newton. Modern mathematics is so abstract that only a few specially gifted people seem competent to add to it. No animal has ever come close in technological progress: in discovering new techniques, in refining and perfecting old ones. Bees still make combs to store their honey in the same way they have done for millions of years.

Another aspect of human originality is found in the world's literature. Here the ability of humans to imagine and to fantasize has given birth to great masterpieces such as the *Iliad*, the *Odyssey*, the *Aeneid*, the *Divine Comedy*, Shakespeare's dramas, and so forth. No animal, not even the chimp, has created a literature.

Still another difference between humans and other animals is that humans have a sense of morality. They are deeply concerned with what is right and what is wrong in human behavior. As far as we can tell, no animal ever reflects on whether what it is about to do is morally right or wrong. It is programmed by its heredity and experience to do what benefits it and its species and to avoid what does not. Thus the great devotion of a mother fox for its young is truly amazing, but she cannot help acting so. A dog can be trained to do or to avoid some action by its owner, using a system of rewards and punishments. When it has failed to act according to its owner's wishes, it may show awareness of its transgression by putting its tail between its legs and "begging" for forgiveness in order to avoid punishment. But true moral judgments are impossible for animals because such judgments presuppose an awareness of ethical principles. To formulate such principles is beyond an animal's capabilities. Animals have not arrived at a "Ten Commandments for Animals." Further, for ethical principles to have any meaning, one must presuppose the freedom to act or not to act in accord with them. Animals act according to their drives, their instincts. What in humans would be conscious self-sacrificing behavior, like that of the worker-bees gathering nectar for the nourishment of the larvae in the hive, is purely for them instinctive behavior.

A final scientific difference between humans and all other animals is that human evolution is now preeminently an evolution of culture. Although each newborn has to learn the culture of its parents, the fact is that he or she has no need to build it up from scratch. Each generation preserves its culture and adds to it so that it seems to have a life of its own. Once this was done by

word of mouth but, with the invention of writing, the achievements of culture could be handed down, first on parchments,
papyri, and stones or clay tablets, later on in printed books and
films and by various electronic means such as audio and video
tapes. No animal records its culture and passes it on to succeeding
generations in any form. The favorable behavior responses that
have been acquired by animals in the course of their evolution are
somehow inscribed in their heredity. Thus most behavior of
animals is stereotyped and fixed. There is some possibility for
learning from changed circumstances. This is most evident in the
mammals, especially in the apes. Imitation is often involved.
Thus a monkey in Japan started to wash its food in the ocean,
perhaps by chance, and liked the result. Soon members of its
troop imitated him and did the same. The passing on of this
behavior to succeeding generations can be explained by imitation of the behavior of the older members of the troop by the
younger members.

As a result of all the above considerations, one can understand how incorrect it is to say and believe that man is nothing
more than a naked ape. Perhaps the anthropologist who said this
only wished to remind us of our animal ancestry. We are certainly
not angelic spirits. In many of our vital activities we are not
superior to our animal forebears. This is certainly true of our
unconscious metabolic processes like digestion, blood circula-
tion, and so forth. But when we are conscious of what we are
doing and can reflect on it, we can transform what is purely
instinctive activity in animals to something expressive of our
superior status to any animal. I say "can" because humans are quite
capable of never rising much above the level of animal behavior
in actions which they share with brute beasts. Humans, though,
*can* make their actions human, which no animal can ever do.

From all the evidence available to them, especially the
increasing amount of data from fossil discoveries, anthropologists feel quite confident in asserting that humans evolved and

only over some millions of years acquired the physical and mental characteristics of modern *Homo sapiens*. What evoked and promoted human evolution from an ape-like ancestor to the present unique state? In their answer anthropologists turn to the factors involved in the evolution of any animal. That is, they apply Darwin's theory of natural selection as previously explained. The first changes on the way to human status were the anatomical alterations required to permit habitual erect posture. Modern apes can readily stand and walk erect, for instance when needed to carry something in their arms. But they cannot do this for any prolonged time without tiring. Their bones and muscles are not well adapted for bipedal walking or standing. The changes in humans which adapt them for habitual erect posture were many. The brain case is set over the center of gravity of the body with its opening (the foramen magnum) for the connection with the spinal cord moved forward and below the brain case. The heavy neck muscles previously needed to support the head when it projected forward are now greatly reduced. The spinal column is changed from a simple horizontal arch to a series of vertical curves. The pelvis is widened and provides a basin for support of the abdominal viscera. The support for the entire body once shared by the forelimbs is now provided solely by the hindlimbs. As a result the buttock and thigh muscles are now far more massive than in an ape. Also the femur is straightened and the bones of the foot altered. The big toe is moved from a splayed position to one alongside the others to assist in maintaining stability and to aid in propulsion. The metatarsals and other foot bones are rearranged so as to provide shock absorbing arch supports. These are the more notable changes involved in the transition from a quadrupedal stance and locomotion to one that is bipedal.

These changes had to be hereditary, so mutations in the numerous genes involved had to occur. It is extremely improbable that all the necessary mutations occurred at the same time.

Rather a key mutation facilitating some degree of erect posture occurred first. Such a mutation might have been one involving the structure of the pelvis and attached buttock muscles. Gene mutations for the other changes would accumulate gradually as they served to complete and perfect erect posture. If these postural changes provided its possessor with some advantages for survival and reproduction in its environmental niche, then the genetic changes producing them would be preserved and passed on to descendants. This in essence is what is meant here by natural selection. In Pliocene times in Africa in the areas where the Australopithecine remains are found, the environment was changing from unbroken forests to woodlands with open spaces (savannas). Thus a new environment was open to apes dwelling in the forest trees. To exploit this new opportunity, some abandoned an arboreal way of life for a terrestrial one. Living in the open away from immediate access to trees for safety from predators may have favored the ability to escape by rapid bipedal locomotion. Anthropologists can propose only more or less plausible speculations like this one why the change to an upright bipedal posture was favored. There is no direct evidence available. An erect posture would allow much wider observation of the open spaces furnished by the savannas. Thus predators could be detected from afar and, contrariwise, if the Australopithecines hunted, they could perceive their prey from afar. However some anthropologists, basing their contention on the dentition of the Australopithecines adapted to a vegetarian diet, think they primarily if not exclusively lived on the seeds and fruits gathered from savanna plants. An important advantage favoring a bipedal posture was the freeing of the hands to make and use tools. But for several millions of years of their existence the Australopithecines may have made no stone tools. These are first definitely found with remains of *Homo habilis*. Some anthropologists think that the Australopithecines were scavengers rather than hunters. Rapid bipedal locomotion would confer the ability to move quickly over wide distances in following migrating herds for dead animals. The scavengers, presumed to be the males, could readily move their home bases (women and children) as they traveled along with the animal herds. All this is pure speculation, however.

Once an erect posture was achieved, the next important change in human evolution was increase in brain size and complexity. Increase in brain size is clear from the capacities of the brain-cases preserved, and details of these have been already given in the previous chapter. G.L. Stebbins has noted that the increases in brain size apparently came in spurts. About 3 million years ago the cranial capacity was 500 cc., 2 million years ago it was 700 cc., 500 thousand years ago 900 cc. In between spurts of rapid increase, the cranial capacity remained stable for hundreds of thousands of years. During the last 500 thousand years the increase to the modern average cranial capacity of 1400 cc. occurred much more rapidly, but still in spurts separated by periods of stability lasting 80 to 100 thousand years. An increase in brain size meant an increase in the corresponding number of neurons. Thus the brain could retain, process, and interpret vastly more pieces of information about the surroundings. But the increase in number of brain neurons affected parts of the brain differently. The great increase has been in the frontal, parietal, and temporal lobes of the brain. These areas are involved in memory, association, and speech. As these areas developed, the hominids were able to progress from communication based on grunts and gesticulations to a symbolic spoken language. They were also able to develop the manual dexterity needed to fashion increasingly sophisticated tools. It is by no means coincidental that along with the increase in brain size and complexity, the hominids developed better and better tools. But the relationship is reciprocal. Tool use favored hominids with brains capable of improvements in making them and designing new tools. As brain size and complexity approached the level of modern man, human evolution became dominated by cultural evolution. No longer were humans limited by reliance on chance gene mutations to adapt to varied environments. They invented various technological solutions to the problems which life in different environments proposed. Thus humans did not undergo physical adaptive radiation into different species as is so commonly observed in other animals, except to the very limited extent of racial differentiation. Yet physical evolution probably still continues, favoring humans with brains best capable of exploiting the opportunities opened up by modern technical advances such as the computer.

In our overview of the stages and factors involved in the emergence of modern man from a pre-human ancestry, we should distinguish factual data supported by evidence from their interpretation. The amount of data increases from day to day and establishes firmly that humans gradually evolved to their present state. Natural science must consider humans, though the supreme manifestation of the natural world, still a part of it. Thus natural science explains human evolution by the same factors operative in the evolution of any living creature: genetic variation and selection by the environment of those variants better adapted to it. Natural science proposes as adequate a purely natural process to explain the origin of modern man. Earlier we noted the several ways in which humans are entirely unique in the world of life. Natural science explains these unique properties of humans as resulting at least in part from the organization of the brain, in the tremendously complicated way in which many billions of neurons are interconnected and interact with each other. Natural scientists admit that just how the mind (mental activities) affects the body (chemical and physical activities in the brain) and vice versa remains an unsolved problem, the so-called mind-body problem. Some lessen the problem for themselves by assuming that mental activities are reducible to chemical and physical activities.

Humans have learned through philosophy and especially divine revelation of another aspect of themselves which must elude natural science. Though part of the material world and subject to its laws, human beings have an immaterial aspect. Philosophy has seen as a proof of this that humans can elicit abstract concepts that are independent of matter, such as the concepts of beauty, truth, and goodness. Divine revelation as given especially in the Scriptures makes it clear that humans are essentially superior to other animals because they have spiritual souls. By this is meant that the principle by which humans are what they are, i.e., rational animals, is a principle intrinsically independent of matter. This implies that the soul continues to exist even when the matter, the physical body, to which it is joined, dies, that is, can no longer support the organization and activities characteristic of life.

The new *Catechism of the Catholic Church*, after speaking of the fact that from the beginning of time God simultaneously created from nothing two orders of creatures, the spiritual and the bodily, that is, the angelic and the earthly, and then the human person who shares in both orders, states: "The human person, created in the image of God is both a bodily and a spiritual being. In symbolic language Scripture tells us 'the Lord God formed man from the dust of the earth, and then breathed into his nostrils the breath of life and man became a living being' [Gn 2:7]." [362] "The human *body* shares in the dignity of God's image: it is a *human* body precisely because it is animated by a *spiritual soul*. The whole human person is intended to become, in the body of Christ, a temple of the Spirit. Body and soul, but truly one, man, in his corporeal condition, brings together in himself the elements of the material world which culminate in him and freely praise their Creator. It is therefore forbidden for man to despise his bodily life. On the contrary, he must esteem and respect his body which has been created by God and destined to be raised on the last day [GS 14]." [364]

# The Uniqueness of Humans

Each human as he or she exists is a unit. We must not conceive them as a body inhabited and directed by the soul as something completely separate. Rather we must think of each person as a unit in which the material aspect we see (the body) owes its vital properties to the spiritual aspect we cannot see or touch (the soul). This is what the scholastic philosophers meant when they said that the human soul is the "form" of the human body. Just how the human soul as a spiritual non-material entity can be intimately united to the material of the body so as to be the ultimate ground of its vital activities is difficult to explain. The body cannot exist as a living human body without its soul, yet the soul — because it is essentially immaterial (spiritual) — can and will continue to exist when its body as a human body dies.

If the human soul is immaterial, it cannot owe its existence to matter. We must conclude, therefore, and the Christian faith teaches us, that whenever a human soul comes into existence, it is God, the Supreme Being, who creates it and that out of no preexisting material. Again, the *Catechism of the Catholic Church*: "The Church teaches that every spiritual soul is created immediately by God. The soul is not 'produced' by the parents." [366] We will get back to this point in the following paragraph. Precisely when the human soul is created by God in the ontogeny of every human is not clear. Thomas Aquinas, subscribing to the Aristotelian idea that during the development of the human in its mother's womb successive souls (vegetative, sensitive, rational) "informed" it as it grew, thought that only with the rational soul was a human soul present. Aquinas' opinion is now of historical interest only. Catholic theologians today think that the human soul is created by God when the male and female gametes unite to form the zygote, the single cell which proliferates to form the embryo and its supporting membranes. Speculation on the part of some holds that this takes place about 14 days later, when the primary axis of an embryo is laid down. This last view has support

101

in the idea that as long as twinning is possible, the human soul is not yet present. Only after definitely only one or more embryos are developing from the original zygote would the human soul or souls be created. The official teaching of the Catholic Church in the matter is that life — human life — begins at the moment of conception and, therefore, any attempt to destroy that life (e.g., by use of the "Morning-After Pill") is morally wrong: "Even if a doubt existed concerning whether the fruit of conception is already a human person, it is objectively a grave sin to risk murder" (*Acta Apostolicae Sedis* 66 (1974) 730-744).

What then is the role of the parents in generating their child? Are they merely the "parents" of the body and therefore not really of their child as a human being? They are not generating only a body, not even only a human body. They are generating a particular human person with such and such characteristics inherited from them. In doing this, they require divine cooperation in achieving a result superior to the possibilities of their own causality, a rational human person with a spiritual soul. This result would not occur without the parents' generative activity. They can be truly called and are the parents of their child. Just how God "cooperates" in achieving the result is a very subtle philosophical question well explored by Karl Rahner to whose treatise (see the Suggested Readings at the end of this chapter) the reader is referred. Suffice it to say here that God should be thought of as the "ground," the ultimate basis of the parents' causality enabling them to generate a rational being with a soul, endowed with their heredity. God should not be thought of as a co-cause of the result, much less as intruding "miraculously" in the course of events.

The reader may wonder and be puzzled about the reason for this discussion about the immaterial aspect of every human being, the soul, and the essential role of God in its origin whenever a human being is generated. This discussion has been intended to show that the account of the evolutionary origin of modern *Homo sapiens* is incomplete if it restricts itself to the factors proposed by the natural scientist, viz., genetic variation and natural selection. Incomplete because the account necessarily ignores the spiritual aspect of every human person, that each person has an immortal non-material soul which cannot be the effect of the unaided natural factors proposed by natural scientists. But not false if the account admits that it is only explaining the origin of man as a part of the animal world. The Christian believer can and should accept the factual data found by anthropologists which support the evolution of *Homo sapiens* over time. But the Christian believer finds God acting throughout, but not in a way that natural scientists must reject. The Christian believer knows that nothing exists, nothing acts without God's supporting causality. Thus God, the primary cause behind the whole process of human evolution as the Creator, is the primary cause of all cosmic processes. This causal activity of God is never accessible to the methods and tools of natural science, and cannot be considered by it in constructing its theories and in collecting its data.

Up to the origin of the first true human with a spiritual soul, no special creative activity of God would be required. Previous to this point in human evolution the generation of more and more advanced hominids would require no activity of God beyond that necessary for the origin of any other animal. When was this point in human evolution reached? In general, one might say that such a point was reached when the evolving brain reached a level of complexity capable of supporting at least the beginnings of the mental activities we have noted as found uniquely in *Homo sapiens*: the use of language in communicating, a consciousness of self, a reflective awareness of time and beauty, and a true sense of morality. Was this level reached in *Homo habilis*? His brain was still probably well below the necessary level. In *Homo erectus*? Maybe. In *Homo neanderthalensis*? Very likely yes, because he had a sufficiently well developed brain, was aware of death and tried to provide for his dead in an afterlife. In *Homo sapiens* (Cro-Magnon man)? Certainly here, for he had a brain equal in every way to our own. His cultural achievements in arts and crafts, considering the times and the materials available, equal those of modern man living today.

To sum up, the Christian believer and the natural scientist need not be in contradiction in how they interpret human evolution. They explain and interpret it at different levels. The natural scientist (anthropologist) tries to explain human evolution in terms of natural factors accessible to natural science and may not be able to detect any plan or purpose behind it. The Christian believer, having access to information from divine revelation, sees God working through these natural factors to produce a being capable of knowing, loving and serving God and of sharing in His own Divine Life.

## SUGGESTED READINGS

1. *Catechism of the Catholic Church*, Most Rev. Cristoph Schönborn, Gen. ed. (Boston, MA: St. Paul Editions, 1994).

2. Gardner, B.T. and R.A. Gardner, "Two-way Communication with an Infant Chimpanzee," *Behavior of Nonhuman Primates*, A. Schrier and F. Stollnitz, eds., v. 4: pp. 117-184 (New York, NY: Academic Press, 1971).

3. Gibbons, Ann, "Déjà Vu All Over Again: Chimp-language Wars," *Science*, v. 263: pp. 1561-1562, 1992.

4. Goodall, Jane, *Through a Window: My Thirty Years with the Chimpanzees of Gombe* (New York, NY: Houghton-Mifflin, 1990).

5. Hogan, Richard M. and John LeVoir, Section B: "Human Beings and the World," pp. 31-41 of "God's Love: Creation," in *Faith for Today: Pope John Paul II's Catechetical Teachings* (New York, NY: Doubleday, 1988).

6. Lawick-Goodall, Jane Van, *In the Shadow of Man* (New York, NY: Houghton-Mifflin, 1971).

7. Lindern, Eugene, "Can Animals Think?" in *Time*, v. 141: pp. 54-61, 1993.

8. Premack, David and Ann James Premack, "Teaching Language to an Ape," *Scientific American*, v. 245: pp. 92-99, 1972.

9. Rahner, Karl, *Hominisation: The Evolutionary Origin of Man as a Theological Problem* (New York, NY: Herder and Herder, 1965).

10. Rumbaugh, D.M. et al., "Reading and Sentence Completion by a Chimpanzee (Pan)," *Science*, v. 182: pp. 731-733, 1973.

11. Stebbins, G. Ledyard, *Darwin to DNA, Molecules to Humanity*, (San Francisco, CA: W.H. Freeman, 1982).

12. Terrace, Herbert et al., "Can an Ape Create a Sentence?" in *Science*, v. 206: pp. 891-902, 1979.

CHAPTER 12

# The Origins of Religion and Morality: Sociobiology

This chapter necessarily treats the origins of religion and morality in a very limited way. Obviously to do so in any adequate way would require a whole library of books. The goal here is much more modest: it is to examine some explanations of religion and morality proposed by sociobiologists and to see how far they can be accepted by a person with religious faith.

What religion is could be defined in several ways, but for our purposes religion includes the belief that beings exist superior to humans and also the efforts to interact with them. Morality here means the evaluation of human actions as good or evil according to some norms.

The earliest humans have left no written records from which we could learn of their religious attitudes and practices. Study of the 400 thousand year old Terra Amata site in Nice, France, shows that the first humans, *Homo erectus*, lived there in bands of 15-20 individuals made up of 2-3 households. These lived in temporary crude huts in close proximity and hunted large animals (elephants, deer, and wild boars). We learn nothing of

107

these people's religious beliefs but we can reasonably infer, supposing that they were rational beings, that they had formulated some kind of moral code. Stable life together would require rules regulating acceptable sexual relationships (pair bonding, incest taboos and the like), cooperation in hunting and the equitable sharing of resources.

Neanderthal man has left us strong evidences of some kind of religious beliefs. He believed in life after death. This can be inferred from the care he used to inter his dead and especially from instances where flint implements and food were placed in the grave. A particularly instructive case is that of a 60-thousand-year-old burial site found in the Shanidar cave in Iraq. Here a man whose skull had been crushed apparently in an accident was laid on a bed of freshly picked flowers, wild forms of blue grape hyacinths, golden ragwort, bachelor's buttons, and hollyhocks, inferred from the kinds of fossil pollen found below the skeleton. The same man had survived the amputation of his right arm at the elbow many years before. Evidently Neanderthal man could show affection and care for a partly disabled member of their race.

Neanderthal man apparently practiced at least in some cases a religious cult of bears. He often resided in caves and had to drive out the bears that occupied them. He ate the meat of bears but apparently felt a need to propitiate their spirits. For example, in a cave in eastern Austria, the inhabitants arranged inside a rectangular stone inclosure about three feet in height seven cave-bear skulls with their muzzles all pointed to the cave entrance.

We presume that Neanderthal man, like *Homo erectus* and for the same reasons, had a code of conduct governing social life. However there is clear evidence from several sites that he engaged in warfare. Thus the pelvis of one was pierced by a spear. A spear point was found in the rib cage of another. At the Krapina site in northwestern Yugoslavia bone fragments from at least a dozen individuals have been found in a cave hearth. The long bones had been subjected to fire and were cracked open along their entire length, ostensibly to get at the marrow. It may be that Neanderthal man at times cannibalized the remains of slain foes.

We encounter next fully modern *Homo sapiens*. The best known early representative, Cro-Magnon man, has left abundant remains attesting to the high level of culture he achieved. Below a limestone cliff overlooking Les Eyzies along the Dordogne river in France several families had arranged their hearths in a row under one roof. This site is estimated to be 23,000 years old. About 10,000 years later, further down the river, a much larger community estimated to number 400-600 persons occupied shelters placed side by side along about a two mile stretch of river bank. Large communities like these we can be sure could not exist without a community-accepted code of conduct.

Did Cro-Magnon man have any kind of religion? Since we have no written records, we must examine the cultural remains available for evidence. Cro-Magnon man depended for survival on hunting a great variety of animals (reindeer, wild cattle, bison, wild horses, woolly rhinoceroses, mammoths, wild goats, wild boars, and cave bears). He depicted these with great artistic skill on the walls and ceilings of caves. Frequently the animals were represented with arrows or spears sticking in them. From this circumstance, reasoning by analogy with similar practices of primitive peoples still surviving, anthropologists have speculated that Cro-Magnon man practiced a kind of magic religion: the representation of a kill would bring success in the actual hunt. One of their number might have acted as a kind of tribal "priest" in rituals involving these representations. Some cave paintings and engravings appear to image such a "witch doctor." One of the most suggestive is that of a bearded man carrying reindeer antlers on his head and clothed in an animal skin ending in a horse's tail. The relationship of the people with the "forces of nature," the causes of things, the supernatural and the hereafter were highly complex and often expressed in rituals presided over by a shaman who was thought to have special powers. The many statuettes of the human female in which the genital area and the breasts are emphasized may represent fetishes which were used in these ceremonies to ensure female fertility.

When humans learned to cultivate various kinds of plants and to domesticate various animals, they had a dependable source of food and no longer needed to hunt for survival. More important, role diversification was possible. Now some could till the soil and raise domestic animals (farmers, herders). Others could specialize in preparing the food (butchers, bakers). Some could operate shops to sell the food (shop-keepers). Still others could be occupied in transporting food from a site of abundance to another in need (teamsters). With the physical needs of the group provided for, some humans were free to engage in all sorts of the civilized arts (painting, music, sculpture). Writing was invented and scribes set to record, among other matters, business transactions and tax receipts. Villages favorably situated on rivers or harbors grew to densely populated cities. Ruins of these first foci of modern urban civilization are scattered over the globe and have been excavated and studied by numerous archaeologists. Thus we know a great deal about the beliefs and customs of their inhabitants. All practiced elaborate forms of religion, frequently in imposing temples. Typically they worshipped a pantheon of gods, often with one raised over the rest. A special caste of priests and priestesses preserved the religious traditions and rituals for the worship of the gods. These first civilized peoples had systems of morality governing all aspects of their lives. One of the best known is the Code of Hammurabi (circa 1780 B.C.) in ancient Mesopotamia. From all these facts, there is no doubt that civilized people at the very beginning of recorded history were believers and practitioners of some form of religion and morality.

Students of the origin of religion and morality have also

turned to the examination of existing or recently extinct primitive peoples for clues. There is now general agreement that all of these peoples have or had some form of religion, be it only some kind of religious magic or taboos. Thus from the fact that humans as far as known have always practiced some kind of religion we can conclude that they have a strong propensity for religion. This is to say that to have some kind of religion is rooted in the very nature of a rational human being. No animal has any form of religion. Religion is a uniquely human activity.

Over the years, scientists who are not believers have adopted various attitudes towards the origin of religion. Some have taken the view that religion was invented by primitive man to provide for him some explanation as to why the world of nature, including himself, existed. These explanations were fictions based on ignorance of the true bases of natural phenomena. According to this view, modern science would expect humans to abandon religion as the illusory creation of their racial childhood. Humans should realize that they stand alone without support from gods or goddesses and are free to fashion their own norms of acceptable conduct (morality). This extreme attitude has been trenchantly championed by the well-known Nobel prize-winning microbiologist and geneticist Jacques Monod (1910-1976) in his best seller *Chance and Necessity* (1972), a philosophical study of science in the modern world.

Other non-believing scientists are not as sure as Monod that religion has no relevance for modern scientific man. They are impressed with the failures of various rival systems such as Marxism to eradicate religion from the people of the world and they have observed that such attempts often merely substitute one cult for another, e.g., in the case of Marxism, the veneration of the State or its leaders (Lenin or Mao) for the veneration of some supernatural being (God). These scientists have concluded that to have some kind of religion is an ineradicable part of human nature. Since these scientists think that human nature is entirely a product of evolution, they speculate how natural selection, the driving force of evolution, could have favored and promoted the impulse to religion in humans.

One of these speculators who have sought the origins of religion and morality in evolution is Edward O. Wilson (1929- ). In a number of books and articles (especially in his *Sociobiology: The New Synthesis*, 1975) he has defended the view that the bases of all forms of human social behavior, including religion, must be found in biology, specifically in evolution. Sociobiology is the name given by Wilson for the scientific study of the biological basis of all forms of social behavior in all kinds of organisms, including *Homo sapiens*.

Wilson's basic ideas on the origin of religion and morality can be summarized in a couple of sentences. Religious practices which enhanced survival and procreation of their practitioners have favored the survival and spread of the genes responsible for programming the systems (nervous, sensory, hormonal) involved in the adoption of religious practices. The result has been that after thousands of human generations the predisposition to religious beliefs may have become an ineradicable part of human nature, conceived by Wilson as the set of genetically programmed behavioral predispositions characterizing humans.

Wilson is a sociobiologist, but more basically he is a "scientific materialist." As such he believes that all phenomena of the universe, including the human mind, have a material basis, are subject to the same physical laws, and can be most deeply understood by scientific analysis. According to Wilson, scientific materialism has steadily eroded the bases of religious beliefs until all that is left is the concept of God as the First Cause of all physical phenomena. This concept, admits Wilson, will always remain impregnable to the analysis of scientific materialism. Thus according to Wilson the belief in a personal moral God cannot be expected to disappear.

According to Wilson, three great mythologies are competing for the allegiance of mankind. One such mythology is Marxism (dialectical materialism). Marxism represents history as involving an inevitable class struggle to be ended by seizure of control of production by the workers and the establishment of a classless society. Economic forces are supposed to dominate the behavior and institutions of humans throughout history. Humans are supposed to be endowed with few innate drives and thus can be readily molded to pursue the goals of the Marxist social state. Marxists deny strong genetic biases regarding human behavior. Wilson dismisses the mythology of Marxism as founded on inadequate, even false concepts of human nature. By denying strong genetic constraints on human nature, Marxism falls afoul of the discoveries of human sociobiology.

Traditional religion, according to Wilson, constitutes the second mythology. Sociobiology explains the disposition to embrace a religious mythology as a completely material phenomenon genetically programmed into human nature because of its past selective value. The possibility exists, according to Wilson, that this innate disposition toward a religious mythology giving meaning and purpose to human life can be exploited by the third great mythology, that of scientific materialism.

Scientific materialism presents its own epic: the evolution of the universe from the "Big Bang" 15 billion years ago to the origins of the elements, the galaxies, life, the human mind. Physical laws governing this grand epic of evolution are believed to apply throughout the universe, but Wilson admits that this belief cannot be rigorously proved. Thus we have here also a mythology. Science has liberated modern man by giving him knowledge and some degree of dominion over himself and the environment. As expressed in the mythology of scientific materialism, according to Wilson, it can appeal to the deepest needs of human nature for some purpose and goal to human life. However, ultimately, Wilson concedes, it can offer only a blind hope in a better future than the present for humans.

Another contemporary sociobiologist is Richard D. Alexander. In his recent book *The Biology of Moral Systems*, he expresses views similar to those of Wilson. Alexander regards as basic to evolution the survival by reproduction of genes. Natural selection acts to maximize the survival not only of certain copies in given favored individuals and their direct descendants but also of copies of these genes in collateral relatives. These individuals seek their self-interest which is realized by maximizing the survival and spread of their genes. This, according to Alexander, is the explanation of why they seek to create descendants and assist relatives to do the same. This altruism shown to relatives is extended to non-relatives because of the advantage the individuals stand to gain from them in their goal of perpetuating their genetic endowments. However, since individuals in a given group are genetically unique and each strives to transmit his or her genetic endowment, conflicts arise. According to Alexander, moral rules spring up to resolve these conflicts. Thus the individuals in a group, related or not, are able to live and to work together. Their unity enables the group to compete successfully with other groups in the same species. Thus morality systems are favored by natural selection.

Alexander thinks that the concept of a god was originally generated and maintained to further the interests of one group at the expense of another. Worshipping the same god acted as a powerful unifying force for the group and thus for its success in competition (even in warfare) against other groups. Thus the invention of the idea of a god as the patron of the group was favored by natural selection. The notion itself of a being superior to any human according to Alexander, arose out of the experience of some humans claiming greater rights than others (husbands over wives, parents over children, the strong over the weak). Somehow, Alexander continues, the concept that each different group had its own god or gods evolved into the concept of a universal impartial God for all groups. This God could function as a powerful unifying force for the different groups which acknowledged and worshipped the same God.

To sociobiologists Alexander and Wilson the concept of "god" is a human invention, useful in man's evolution but still with no objective reality. Other non-believing scientists, impressed by the overall orderliness of the universe as governed by laws of nature, think that it is reasonable to hold that there is a mental component to the universe which we may call God. The physicist Freeman Dyson is a good example. He finds evidence of the operations of mind in the universe at three levels. The first level is shown in the elementary physical processes studied in quantum mechanics. In quantum mechanics, matter is found not to be inert but active, constantly "choosing" between alternative possibilities of state according to probabilistic laws. To make choices is a property to some extent of every electron. The second level is found in the activity of the human mind. Here the operations of mind are the object of human experience. Dyson believes that human brains are devices which amplify the mental component of the quantum choices made by molecules in the brain. The third level of mind is seen in the universe as a whole. There it is manifested in what we call the laws of nature.

To Dyson, the third level of mind in the universe may be called God. Dyson's God is a kind of world soul or world mind. He is neither omniscient nor omnipotent. He learns and grows as the universe develops. Chance exists because God shares our ignorance. But God uses chance to achieve divine ends. What are these ends? What is the ultimate purpose of the universe? The problem here is to "read" God's mind. What are the answers to the questions: Why do we suffer? Why is the world unjust? What can be the purpose of pain and tragedy? According to Dyson, a possible answer could be that the universe is constructed by God to achieve maximum diversity, to make it as interesting as possible. The result is that life is possible on earth but faces all kinds of challenges (comet impacts, ice ages, plagues, nuclear

115

weapons, sin, death). Not all challenges can be overcome and the result is tragedy.

In giving the views of sociobiologists and other non-Christian believers like Dyson on religion, I have omitted the views of scientists who are Christians and see no problem in being simultaneously Christian believers and natural scientists. Some of these keep their religious and scientific views in separate compartments with no mutual interaction. Others try to integrate their religious and scientific ideas into one unified understanding of the meaning of reality. Perhaps the most notable practitioner of this second approach was the paleontologist and priest Teilhard de Chardin (1881-1955). He saw all creation evolving from the simplest physical beginnings to higher and higher states of consciousness according to a law of complexity-consciousness: the more complex the state of organization of matter, the higher its state of consciousness. Humans are the highest material achievement of this law to date. Teilhard finds love to be the attraction behind this rise to greater and greater consciousness which culminates in what he refers to as the "Omega Point," which is identical with God. Teilhard believed that by his love, this Omega-God is now engaged in a "mega-synthesis" to unite all mankind into a new conscious entity centered around itself. The end of the evolutionary process is most clearly manifest in the person of the cosmic Christ. The views of Teilhard have gained qualified approval by some eminent scientists, for example, the geneticist Theodosius Dobzhansky. These admire his fascinating portrayal of the history of evolution, but have serious reservations about its scientific bases. Thus they find him resuscitating the rejected theory of Lamarck by his emphasis on the "within," the psyches of organisms, as guiding the forward and upward march of evolution. Some scientists, for example Jacques Monod, have denounced Teilhard for confusing faith and science. Teilhard has found his most enthusiastic adherents — and perhaps his

116

severest critics — among believers. His supporters, not particularly critical of the scientific bases of his ideas, find them consoling and inspiring. Consoling because they neutralize their fears that the discoveries of science have destroyed the bases of their religious faith. Inspiring because they restore a direction and goal to human endeavors. His opponents find his ideas tainted with a view of reality which borders on a form of pantheism which excludes or misinterprets original sin and betrays a certain lack of appreciation for the redemptive role of Christ, his passion and death on the cross. Neither position probably does justice to the thought of one of the truly original philosopher-paleontologists of our time.

Returning to the views of the sociobiologists, they assume that human evolution is similar to the evolution of higher animals, so that conclusions arrived at by studies of animal behavior can be applied with little change to human behavior. Back of this assumption is a principle called "inclusive fitness." According to this principle, in both animals and humans new patterns of behavior can only become established if they enable their practitioners to produce more healthy progeny than non-practitioners. This, of course, is a straight-forward application of Darwin's principle of natural selection to the genesis of animal behavior. Religious behavior and moral systems became established in humans because they contributed to their "inclusive fitness."

A paradigmatic example of how sociobiologists transfer insights gained from the study of animal behavior to provide explanations of human behavior comes from their study of insect societies. Sociobiologists have studied in great detail and depth the behavior of bees, ants and termites. From these studies they have derived an explanation of why altruism in insect colonies was favored by natural selection. For example, sterile honeybee workers labor industriously to provide nectar and pollen for the bee colony, and when the colony is invaded, they die in its defence. Since these workers die without leaving their own genes to progeny, it would seem that their altruistic behavior could not be maintained by Darwinian natural selection. However, the genes of the workers are also possessed by the queen, which does transmit the genes of the workers to the next generation. Thus the self-sacrificing labor of the workers makes possible the devotion of the queen solely to reproduction of the genes shared by the queen and the workers. Natural selection has favored the progress and survival of the colony as a unit, of which the workers and the queen form essential parts. As we have noted above, sociobiologists explain altruism shown in human societies in an analogous manner, viz., natural selection favors altruism shown to relatives because it contributes to the individual's "inclusive fitness" in that it increases the probability that his or her genes present also in relatives will be transmitted to future generations.

What can the Christian believer accept from the sociobiologists? As we have observed in previous chapters, he or she can accept the evidence for human evolution from pre-human ancestors. Looked at from a purely natural standpoint, commonly accepted religious beliefs no doubt helped the first humans to band together in groups larger than those related by kin to provide for themselves the physical means for survival. Also from a purely natural viewpoint, it is reasonable to assume that a system of morality allowing and forbidding some activities had to be accepted by the members of groups in order that they could live and work together.

However sociobiologists over-emphasize the role of genetic factors in the evolution of human behavior. This has been recognized already by some non-believing scientists who accept only natural explanations for human nature and behavior. Sociobiologists tend to neglect the great importance and significance of non-genetic transmission of complex patterns of human behavior (cultural evolution). They also greatly over-emphasize the transmission of one's genes to the next generation as *the* goal aimed at by humans in their lives. Also their reduction of human behavior to equivalent animal behavior leaves them with only selfish motives to account for all aspects of human behavior. That a human would sacrifice much, even life itself, for his personal beliefs is a difficult if not insoluble problem for a sociobiologist. For a Christian who sees in humans much more than an animal, with motives and goals incomprehensible to an animal, this presents no great problem.

To the Christian believer there are a number of fundamental defects in the views of sociobiologists and other non-believing scientists about religion and morality. One of the most basic is in their concepts of God. For them God seems to be identical with "physical reality": the way things are constituted and operate. Thus in part "God" seems to be equated with natural laws, such as, in physics, the law of universal gravitation or, in biology, the "law" of natural selection. The existence of a personal God behind physical reality is either denied or ignored as unknowable. Dyson does propose a personal "god" behind physical reality, but this "god" is limited in powers and knowledge. The evolution of the universe is not completely under his control.

In contrast, to the Christian believer, God is not a part of the world, but is the cause of its becoming into existence (creation). As the cause of its persistence in existence, God is present throughout creation. God always existed and always will exist. There are no limits to God's knowledge (He is omniscient) and no limits to God's power (He is omnipotent). The Christian believer thinks that any normal intelligent human can get some idea about God as the ultimate source of reality from contemplating the world. Thus religious beliefs and practices could have originated simultaneously with the origin of the first rational human being. As we have speculated, this may have been *Homo erectus*, but he has left us no clue to his religious views. *Homo neanderthalensis* did leave us evidence that he believed in an afterlife and so probably had some religious beliefs and practices, though again there are no written records left by him to confirm this idea. No written records either were left by the first completely modern type *Homo sapiens*, but from his artistic remains (cave paintings, carvings, and so forth), we have some evidence of religious practices perhaps only on the level of sympathetic magic and fertility cult. With the advent of urban life, written and archaeological remains leave no doubt that humans had evolved numerous varieties of religious life and practice. To the Christian believer, these are corruptions of the true idea of God given to the first humans in a primordial revelation. We learn that there was a primordial or primitive revelation in the first chapters of Genesis. Revelation from God was needed to give humans a correct idea of God, but apparently this revealed correct idea was very soon lost.

To a Christian believer, a second fundamental defect in the views of scientists mentioned is in their concept of human beings. To them humans are not essentially superior to other animals. Their brain has evolved into a unique collection of billions of neurons interconnected in countless ways. What we call mental activities reflect the activities of this highly organized system of nerve cells as these activities are evoked by internal and external stimuli. "Free will" at most reflects the indeterminacy of the numerous alternative states of the neural pathways governing possible actions. Basically then human nature is material and does not survive death. True, individual human genes may survive preserved in direct or collateral descendants. Sociobiologists can conceive no other immortality for humans.

Natural reason can arrive at some approximation about the true nature of human beings. From the ability to form immaterial concepts like truth, goodness, and beauty, one can infer that the mind eliciting these concepts has a basis in some immaterial entity. Humans are also conscious that they have some measure of freedom to do or not to do certain acts. That something human survives after death can be concluded from the immaterial aspect of human nature. What humans can know about human nature only with difficulty, the Christian believes God has revealed clearly and with certitude. Thus humans have immortal souls which will survive the death of the body. At the end of time, the body will be resurrected and united with the soul to reconstitute the completely human being again. God has destined human beings for eternal life with Him in inexpressible joy and happiness. This goal for human existence cannot be conceived by unaided human powers of reason and cannot be won by unaided human efforts. Thus the human end is truly "supernatural." But already in this life, humans are enabled to share in a limited way in the divine life by the supernatural gift of "sanctifying grace." God also endows humans with gifts that enable them to live and act in a way worthy of their sharing of divine life now and after death. Among these gifts are supernatural faith, hope, and charity.

The revelation that had obscure beginnings at the time of the first humans, and was expanded upon in the revelations made to the patriarchs and prophets of the Old Testament, reached its completion in the life and teachings of Jesus Christ. Christ revealed that the nature of the one God is shared by three divine persons, the Father, the Son, and the Holy Spirit. In the Sermon on the Mount and in numerous parables, Christ tells Christian believers how to live and act to be worthy of the eternal life for which they are destined. The morality presented by Christ is summed up in the two great commandments of love, love of God and love of one's neighbor, even if that neighbor is an enemy. What sociobiologists have struggled to explain on a purely natural level, self-sacrificing love of God and of our brothers and sisters, is no mystery to a Christian believer.

The aim of this work has been to show to a Christian believer that there are no obstacles to his or her faith from the factual discoveries of scientists or from their well-founded theories. Of course we have seen in this chapter that there *are*

obstacles and contradictions to Christian faith in the speculations of materialistic scientists, especially of the sociobiologists.
As we conclude this chapter, we emphasize that Christian beliefs
are founded on bases inaccessible to scientific methods, namely
divine revelation. The knowledge about human beings and God
furnished by this revelation can be freely accepted or freely
rejected. It does not force human acceptance. In fact it is a part
of Christian belief that to believe in God's revelation is itself a gift
from God, a gift that we cannot win by our own efforts. We can
ask for this gift from God and God will not refuse it. This gift of
faith gives to humans the only completely satisfying answer to
the goal of our existence, namely to love and serve God in this life
and to be happy with Him forever in the next.

Unbelievers have complained that this future goal to be
achieved perfectly only in the next life ("pie in the sky") prevents
Christian believers from taking seriously their duties as citizens
of the world here and now. This reproach may have some basis
in the lives of some believers at some times in the history of
Christianity. But today Christians realize more clearly than ever
that they have an obligation to contribute to the progress of
mankind in this world. This progress certainly includes relief
from oppression of every kind and equal access to the goods of
this earth for all. Another complaint of unbelievers is that
Christian believers, in carrying out the divine mandate "to
conquer the earth" and "to be masters of the fish of the sea, the
birds of heaven and all living animals on the earth" as given in the
first chapter of Genesis, have ruthlessly exploited the resources
of the earth with no regard for the common good especially of
future generations. If this reproach has truth in regard to some
Christians, it is because they have misinterpreted God's mandate
as if it encouraged selfish and shortsighted uses of this world's
resources. An interpretation in agreement with all we know of
God's relation to the world He created and sustains is that the
human task is to develop the resources of the world for the benefit

of all. Sound technological progress is certainly in agreement
with God's mandate, but this progress must also be in agreement
with human nature as being responsible for human actions.
These actions must not be against the common good.

## SUGGESTED READINGS

1. Alexander, Richard D., *The Biology of Moral Systems* (New
   York, NY: Aldine de Gruyter, 1987).

2. Austin, William H., "Evolutionary Explanations of Religion
   and Morality: Explaining Religion Away?" pp. 252-
   272 in *Evolution and Creation*, Ernan McMullin, ed.
   (Notre Dame, IN: University of Notre Dame Press,
   1985).

3. Burhoe, Ralph Wendell, "War, Peace, and Religion's
   Biocultural Evolution," pp. 439-472, *Zygon*, v. 21.

4. de Chardin, Teilhard, *The Phenomenon of Man*, tr. Bernard
   Wall (New York, NY: Harper & Row, 1959).

5. Dodson, Edward O., *The Phenomenon of Man Revisited: A
   Biological Viewpoint on Teilhard de Chardin* (New York,
   NY: Columbia University Press, 1985).

6. Dyson, Freeman J., "Butterflies Again," pp. 288-299 in *Infinite
   in All Directions* (New York, NY: Harper & Row,
   1988).

7. Monod, Jacques, *Chance and Necessity: An Essay on the Natural
   Philosophy of Modern Biology*, tr. Austryn Wainhouse
   (New York, NY: Alfred A. Knopf, Inc., 1971).

8. Stebbins, G. Ledyard, "The Genetic and Cultural Heritage
   of Humanity," Ch. 12, and "Sociobiology and
   Human Evolution," Ch. 13 in *Darwin to DNA*,

*Molecules to Humanity* (San Francisco, CA: W.H. Freeman, 1982).

9. Wilson, Edward O., *Sociobiology* (Boston, MA: Harvard University Press, 1975).

10. Wilson, Edward O., *On Human Nature* (Boston, MA: Harvard University Press, 1978).

# CHAPTER 13

# The Interactions of Faith and Science: Is a Synthesis Possible or Desirable?

In the preceding chapters, we have examined conclusions of modern science and have attempted to show that they do not contradict the truths learned by a Christian believer from divine revelation. In this final chapter, we examine the question whether one can go further beyond reconciliation to a synthesis of the two approaches to reality: faith and science.

As a first step, we note that Christian believers and most scientists agree that, outside of the subject, there is an objective reality to be known and understood. They differ, however, in the particular aspects of reality with which they are concerned and the means they use to investigate these aspects. The object of science is physical reality ranging from the subatomic entities to the stellar galaxies. Science makes observations and does experiments to check on the objective validity of its theories on the interrelationships of physical phenomena. It often attempts to express these relationships in the language of mathematics. Tremendous progress has been achieved in scientific understanding with no end in sight. Here I must call attention to a serious philosophical error made by physicists. From the fact that they are unable to determine by their measuring instruments simultaneously the position and the velocity of an electron, for example, they conclude that events on the subatomic level are indeterminate (Werner Heisenberg's [1901-1976] *Uncertainty Principle*). The error here is to conclude from the indeterminacy of their measurements to indeterminacy of the subatomic entities themselves. This particular error is a manifestation of a more general error committed by physicists when they restrict reality to what they can measure. This is a gratuitous assumption. A truly striking aspect of the physical reality studied by scientists is that unexpected findings all have been intelligible and can be rationally understood. Science of itself cannot give an explanation for this fundamental intelligibility of the physical world.

The object of faith is God and His relationship to creation especially to mankind. What faith knows about God and His relationship to the world has come from divine revelation. Progress in understanding this revelation has occurred. Since revelation was made necessarily to humans with a particular level of culture, it needs study to purify it from historically culture-bound aspects to discover its essential ever-valid message. As we have seen, this observation is particularly true about the revelations recorded in the first chapters of Genesis. The refining and purifying process extends also to how the essential content of a revelation is to be formulated to be intelligible by people of a particular time. Catholics believe that Christ revealed that bread and wine becomes His Body and Blood in the Eucharistic consecration of the Mass. This conversion was interpreted by Thomas Aquinas according to the categories of substance and accident of Aristotelian philosophy. This interpretation (known as transubstantiation) is not part of the original revelation. For example, the Eastern Orthodox Churches hold the same teaching about the Eucharist as the Roman Catholic Church, but do not use Aristotelian terminology. However, no Catholic formulation can annul the dogmatic teaching that the Eucharistic consecration effects an ontological change in the bread and wine. In the words of Pope Paul VI, "this unique and truly wonderful change the Catholic Church rightly and properly calls transubstantiation" (*Mysterium Fidei*, 1965).

In contemplating a synthesis of faith and science, one must avoid confusing them. Their immediate objects of study and investigation, as we have noted, are quite different, as also are their methodologies. Yet both faith and science in seeking to understand reality each at its own level can aid one another. An example of this is how modern science can aid the Christian believer to understand personal immortality. Christians believe in an immortality after physical death that will include the body. Physiologists have shown that though the chemical compounds making up the human body are continuously being replaced, the *pattern* of their arrangement in a particular person is retained. It is the pattern that is permanent, not the material constituents. Thus it is at least conceivable that after the dissolution of one's earthly body at death, a new body can be reconstituted in a resurrection from other molecules because the pattern of their arrangement residing in the immortal human soul has not been lost. Similar ideas have found favor with the scientists Davies and Polkinghorne. It must at once be conceded by Christian believers that these scientific considerations do not and cannot provide understanding of the revelation that the resurrection will be with a *glorified* human body, viz., one endowed with very special properties, one of which will be permanent immunity from death.

Faith and science come in direct contact when each examines the beings making up the universe. To a Christian believer these beings are ultimately God's creation and so should show evidence of God's handiwork. In the past Christian believers pointed to the numerous adaptations found in living organisms as proof that God was their immediate author: the proof for the existence of God from design. A famous example of this mode of reasoning is found in William Paley's work *Natural Theology, or Evidences of the Existence and Attributes of the Deity*. Paley (1740-1805) argued that as one who found a watch and inspected its parts all coordinated to achieve the end of marking time, should conclude that an intelligent being was its maker, so also by similar reasoning an observer of the many intricate adaptations on the parts of so many living organisms to their needs should conclude that an intelligent being (God) was their author. This line of argument was upset somewhat when Darwin explained the adaptations of these organisms as the result of a purely natural process, natural selection acting on hereditary changes arising by chance in the organism.

The adaptations shown by organisms to their needs are often amazingly complicated. For an interesting example, consider the defense mechanism of bombardier beetles. These beetles have two identical glands in their abdomens. Each gland consists of two chambers. The larger inner chamber secretes and stores hydroquinones and hydrogen peroxide. The smaller outer chamber produces the enzymes catalase and peroxidase. A canal, ordinarily closed by a valve, connects the two chambers. When the insect is attacked by a toad or other predator, a muscle opens the valve and the contents of the two chambers are mixed. The catalases release oxygen from the hydrogen peroxide. The peroxidases use the oxygen to oxidize the hydroquinones to quinones and much heat is released. The heat causes sudden expansion of the oxygen which sets up considerable pressure. The entire mixture of quinones, enzymes, and oxygen is literally exploded out through a duct leading from the outer chamber to the outside. As a result, the noxious smelling and irritating quinones are sprayed on the attacker. It immediately reacts by rejecting the insect. The entire process is practically instantaneous. Some scientists have felt that Darwin's explanation needs some supplementation to explain fully the more subtle and complicated adaptations such as the defense mechanism of bombardier beetles.

However, these scientists seek more complete and adequate answers from further scientific investigations and rightly reject any recourse to direct intervention on the part of a deity to complete the explanation. Earlier in Chapter 10 we discussed how Darwin's proposal can be reconciled with a creative role for God as the ultimate ground for all reality, including these special adaptations achieved in the course of evolution.

In recent years support for the activity and therefore existence of a rational being responsible for the establishment of the universe has come from the investigations of some astrophysicists. These have noted that the numerous extremely precise initial conditions set down in the first moments of the existence of the universe made possible the eventual emergence of life and humans. The slightest significant deviation from these initial conditions would have made utterly impossible the development of a universe hospitable to the emergence of life and humans. This insight on the part of these physicists has been called the "Anthropic Principle." For the most part, the technical details of the precise initial conditions can be fully understood only by physicists. Here we can give only a couple of instances of the precise initial conditions. In the expansion of matter in the Big Bang, the balance between the force driving things apart and the force drawing them together (gravity) had to be extremely close. If the expansive force were too great, the primordial matter would have kept flying apart and would never have condensed into stars and galaxies. If the force of gravity dominated, the primordial matter would have contracted again and collapsed on itself before any processes leading to life could begin. The right balance between these two forces, to allow the evolution of the universe as we know it, could not deviate from equality more than one part in $10^{60}$!

Another instance of "fine tuning": the difference between the masses of protons and neutrons (actually about one part in a thousand) is critical. If this difference were not almost exactly twice the mass of the electron, all neutrons would have been changed into protons or else all protons would have been converted into neutrons. Either possibility would have made impossible the existence of the elements which are the basis of chemistry and biology and therefore of life as we know it. Many more details of the amazing fine tuning needed to allow the evolution of the universe as it has occurred, including the emergence of life and of humans, can be found in Suggested Reading No. 3 cited at the end of this chapter.

Physicists have offered a number of theories to explain the existence of the fine tuning without recourse to the activity of a rational being. These theories warn the Christian believer not to conclude that the fine tuning "proves" the existence of God. To make this conclusion would be to fall again into the fallacy of invoking a "God-of-the-gaps" to explain what may eventually be explicable entirely by scientific reasoning. However, granted that the phenomena involved in fine tuning do not prove the existence of a God, yet their existence is what a Christian believer would expect from the creative activity of God. Here science and faith at least support each other.

Science and faith necessarily interact when both make assertions about the same subject. These assertions must not contradict each other since logically something cannot be true for faith and false for science or vice versa. Investigations to resolve some apparent contradictions have resulted in a clearer and more profound understanding of what each source of knowledge really can assert. Most helpful in this connection has been the realization that divine revelation as recorded in the Bible was never intended to provide exact scientific information. Such information was only peripheral to the real content of revelation and had to reflect the limited scientific understanding current at the time of the revelation. Thus no argument against an evolutionary origin of the universe and its parts can be reasonably inferred from the creation accounts in the Bible. Here we have an instance of how information provided by modern science has moved the Christian believer to accept a different understanding of how God works in creation.

Another and very significant aspect of the interactions between faith and science is the role of faith to provide enduring value and significance to the work of a scientist. Without faith in a God as the author of this beautiful world and all its wonders, a scientist can see no ultimate meaning for his efforts to understand it. Thus the biologist Jacques Monod felt that the universe had no significance other than that which man arbitrarily gave it and thus had no really ultimate meaning. Similar sentiments have been expressed by the physicist Steven Weinberg. He thought that the more man understands the universe the more devoid of ultimate meaning it appears to him. Such pessimistic sentiments should not surprise us. Science by itself is powerless to provide solutions to the problem of the ultimate meaning of the universe, man included. But faith assures the Christian believer that the universe does have ultimate meaning as the work of a loving God who brought all into existence and sustains all for the benefit of mankind. Humans are to understand the marvels of creation and to use them wisely to love and serve their Creator and eventually as a reward for faithful stewardship are to enjoy and love God forever.

Do the considerations made in this chapter throw light on the possibility or desirability of a synthesis of faith and science? One definition of synthesis is that it is a process producing a new whole from parts. When the chemist synthesizes the compound water from the elements hydrogen and oxygen, no trace of these gases can be detected in the end product. Such a synthesis is neither possible nor desirable between faith and science. In any synthesis of faith and science, both must maintain their identities as distinct avenues to reality with different immediate objects and methodologies. Yet faith and science can and should complement each other to provide a unified completely satisfying picture of all reality. Without faith, science produces a fascinating picture of how the universe is constituted and operates, but it cannot satisfy the deepest yearning of the human spirit for a truly satisfying ultimate goal for its strivings. Without science, faith does provide the ultimate source and meaning of the universe and an ultimate goal for humans, but it does not and cannot provide answers to the details of how the universe is made up and functions. Pope John Paul II has more than once called for a constructive dialogue between scientists and theologians in their common quest to understand the human condition. Indeed, the Pontifical Academy of Science was established with precisely that goal in mind. Scientists and theologians can and should profit from each other's investigations.

One example of how faith and science complement each other can be found in the life of Louis Pasteur (1822-1895). He was an outstanding biologist who made a number of very significant discoveries by his researches, yet during all his scientific career retained the simple faith of a Breton peasant. Pasteur exemplified by his life that faith and science can complement each other to provide truly satisfying goals for one's life. It is ironical that the non-believing scientist Jacques Monod carried on his important researches on the genetic control of metabolism in bacteria in an institution named after Pasteur, the Pasteur Institute. Pasteur did not leave in writing an integration of his faith and science in one all-embracing interpretation of reality. That was attempted by a fellow Frenchman Teilhard de Chardin in his master-work *The Phenomenon of Man*, briefly described in Chapter 12 of the present work. Teilhard based his lyrical account of the ascent from non-living matter to life to man to God (the Omega Point) on what he called "the phenomena" available to all who merely opened their eyes to contemplate reality. Great and inspiring as Teilhard's account is, he has drawn severe criticism from some scientists for injecting his very strong personal faith into his work (the Omega Point to which all evolution of the cosmos converges cannot be known by science). Conversely, Teilhard, as we mentioned, has been criticized by some for allegedly ignoring or misinterpreting some key teachings of the faith. Teilhard's insights tended to blur, perhaps too much, the distinction between what can be discovered by science and what can be known only by faith. However, along with Pasteur and many other Christian scientists, he remains a striking example of integrating faith and science in one's own personal life.

## SUGGESTED READINGS

1. Aneshansley, Daniel J. and Thomas Eisner, "Biochemistry at 100 degrees C.: Explosive Secretory Discharge of Bombardier Beetles (*Brachinus*)," *Science*, 165: pp. 61-63, 1969.

2. Barbour, Ian G., "Ways of Relating Science and Theology," pp. 21-48 in *Physics, Philosophy, and Theology: A Common Quest for Understanding*, Robert J. Russell, William R. Stoeger, S.J., and George V. Coyne, S.J., eds. (Notre Dame, IN: University of Notre Dame Press, 1988).

3. Barrow, John and Frank Tipler, *The Anthropic Cosmological Principle* (Oxford: Clarendon Press, 1986).

4. de Chardin, Teilhard, *The Phenomenon of Man*, tr. Bernard Wall (New York, NY: Harper & Row, 1959).

5. Davies, Paul, *God and the New Physics* (Dent Publishing, 1983).

6. Heisenberg, Werner, *Physics and Philosophy* (London: Allen and Unwin, 1958).

7. Holmes, S.J., *Louis Pasteur* (New York, NY: Dover Publishing, 1961).

8. John Paul II, "Message to the Reverend George V. Coyne, S.J., Director of the Vatican Observatory" in *Physics, Philosophy and Theology: A Common Quest for Understanding*, op. cit.

9. Monod, Jacques, *Chance and Necessity: An Essay on the Natural Philosophy of Modern Biology*, tr. Austryn Wainhouse (New York, NY: Alfred A. Knopf, Inc., 1971).

10. Paley, William, *Natural Theology, or Evidences of the Existence and Attributes of the Deity Collected from the Appearances of Nature*, 11th ed. (London, R. Fauldar and Son, 1807).

11. Polkinghorne, John, *One World: The Interaction of Science and Theology* (Princeton, NJ: Princeton University Press, 1986).

12. Stoeger, William R., "Contemporary Cosmology and Its Implications for the Science-Religion Dialogue," pp. 219-247 in *Physics, Philosophy and Theology: A Common Quest for Understanding*, op. cit.

13. Weinberg, Steven, *The First Three Minutes* (New York, NY: Basic Books, 1977).

# Glossary

ACCIDENT as a technical term from Aristotelian philosophy, means a modification of a substance which cannot exist independently.

ADAPTIVE RADIATION evolutionary separation of the members of a single major group of organisms into a number of types each adapted to some major feature of the environment.

ADENINE a purine base found in deoxyribonucleic and ribonucleic acids.

AGNOSTIC one who holds that neither the existence of God nor His nature can be known.

ALLOPOLYPLOIDY a process in which the chromosome sets of two or more species are combined in one individual.

ALTRUISM concern for the interests of others.

AMINO ACID an organic molecule containing the amino ($NH_2$) and the carboxyl (COOH) groups attached to the same carbon atom in the molecule.

ANGIOSPERM any plant of the botanical class Angiospermae, whose seeds are enclosed in an ovary.

ANTHROPIC PRINCIPLE the view that a world to contain humans must have a very special character in its basic laws and circumstances.

135

ANTHROPOID one belonging to the Anthropoidea, a division of the Primates which includes monkeys, apes, and humans.

ARTIFACT any man-made object.

ASTROPHYSICIST one who studies the origin, constitution, and fate of the heavenly bodies (stars, galaxies, etc.).

AUSTRALOPITHECINE belonging to or related to the genus *Australopithecus* (ape-like creatures walking erect).

BACTERIA typically one-celled microorganisms lacking a nucleus.

BIG BANG the moment in the origin of the Universe when cosmic matter is thought to have exploded from a state of extreme compression.

BIOGENESIS the origin of living organisms.

BIPEDAL walking on the hind-limbs.

BLASTOCYST early stage in mammalian embryogenesis, a hollow ball of cells with a thickening at one pole where the future embryo will develop.

CAUSES (SECONDARY) as distinguished from the Primary or First Cause (God), all the proximate causes found in nature for various effects.

CENTROMERE the region on a chromosome to which the spindle-fibers involved in motion of the chromosome are attached.

CHLOROPLAST an organelle present in plant cytoplasm which contains chlorophyll.

CHORDATE a member of the phylum Chordata which have at some stage of their development a dorsal axial supporting rod (notochord).

CHROMOSOME a linear cellular structure which consists mainly of deoxyribonucleic acid, proteins, and which carries in linear order the genetic factors.

CODON a sequence of three nucleotides in a nucleic acid which codes in polypeptide synthesis for one amino acid or for termination of synthesis.

COELOCANTH a kind of primitive fish with paddle-like fins.

COENZYME a substance essential for the catalytic activity of its corresponding enzyme.

COMPLEXITY-CONSCIOUSNESS (LAW OF) the more complex the state of organization of matter, the higher its state of consciousness.

CONCORDISM the attempt to find scientific explanations for the various steps described in Genesis for divine creation.

CREATIONISM (SCIENTIFIC) the view that divine creation as recorded in Genesis can be proved by scientific evidence.

CYANOBACTERIA primitive procaryotes characterized by a distinctive blue-green pigment.

CYBERNETICS comparative study of the central nervous system and of mechanical electrical communication systems (e.g. computers).

CYTOPLASM the part of a cell outside its nucleus.

CYTOSINE a pyrimidine base found in ribonucleic and deoxyribonucleic acids.

DEIST one who holds that God after originating the world has left it alone to evolve according to its own laws without any further concern of God.

DELETION (GENETIC) loss of a segment of a chromosome or of a part of the sequence of DNA or protein.

DEOXYRIBONUCLEIC ACID (DNA) a molecule consisting of two strands of nucleotides in which the sugar is deoxyribose wound about each other in spiral fashion and held together by bonds between complementary bases.

DEOXYRIBOSE a five carbon sugar found in deoxyribonucleic acid.

DIPLOID an organism or cell with its complement of chromosomes present in duplicate.

DOPPLER EFFECT the variation in the apparent length of waves (sound or light) as the emitting source approaches or recedes from the observer.

DUPLICATION (GENETIC) doubling of a gene or larger segment of a chromosome.

ELECTRON a negatively charged particle found in atoms.

ENTELECHY as conceived by Vitalists, the non-mechanical agency responsible for the existence and activities of a living thing.

ENVIRONMENT all the external conditions surrounding an organism and affecting its survival.

ENZYME an organic molecule which increases the rate of a specific chemical reaction in an organism.

ESTERASE one of a class of enzymes that catalyzes the hydrolysis of esters.

EUCARYOTE an organism in which the chromosomes are separated from the cytoplasm by a membrane.

EVOLUTION hereditary changes in a population of organisms over time which adapt them to changing environments.

FERTILIZATION the union of the male and female gametes to form one cell, the zygote.

FITNESS the reproductive capability of an organism measured by the number of progeny it leaves to the following generation as compared with the average number left by members of its generation.

FOSSIL any material evidence of the life of an organism which has survived to the present.

FUNDAMENTALISM the view that the literal interpretation of the Bible is fundamental to true Christianity.

GAMETE a male or female reproductive cell (sperm or egg) capable of taking part in fertilization.

GENE hereditary factor specifying a biological function.

GENESIS the first book of the Old Testament in the Bible.

GENETIC CODE the triplet sequences of nucleotides in a nucleic acid coding for the amino acids in a protein.

GENETICS the science studying the phenomena and the laws of heredity.

GENOME a basic set of chromosomes which carries all the genes of an organism.

GENOTYPE the genetic constitution of an individual organism.

GEOCENTRIC the view that the earth is the center of the solar system.

GUANINE a purine base found in ribonucleic and deoxyribo-nucleic acids.

GYMNOSPERM a member of the botanical class Gymnospermae whose seeds are not enclosed in an ovary.

HALF-LIFE the time required to convert half of a given amount of a radioactive element to a daughter element.

HAPLOID having only one set of the chromosomes characteristic of a species.

HELIOCENTRIC the view that the sun is the center of the solar system.

HOLISTIC placing the emphasis on wholes rather than on the parts making up the whole.

HOMINID a member of the Hominidae, the family of the Primates which includes all humans, ancient or modern.

HOMINOID a member of the Primate superfamily Hominoidea which includes the families Pongidae (great apes), Hylobatidae (gibbons) and Hominidae (humans).

HOMOLOGOUS having similar structure.

HUMANISM (SECULAR) the view that man is alone in the universe without any need of or support from divine beings to fashion his role and fate.

HYPOTHESIS a provisional explanation for some phenomena of nature.

INFALLIBILITY incapable of any error in a statement.

INSPIRATION (DIVINE) the doctrine that the Scriptures were composed and written under the influence of a special charisma from God.

INVERSION (PERICENTRIC) a reversal of the linear order of a segment of genes including the centromere in a chromosome.

ISOLATING MECHANISMS all factors preventing members of one population of organisms from successfully interbreeding with members of other populations.

ISOMERIC (FORMS OF MOLECULES) differing only in the structural arrangement of the same constituent atoms.

KARYOTYPE the chromosomal constitution of an organism often arranged in diagrammatic form.

LAW (NATURAL) a statement of an invariable order of events observed in nature which involves only physical causation.

LIGHT YEAR the distance traveled by light in one year, approximately six trillion miles.

MASAI a pastoral and hunting tribe of nomads living in Tanganyika and Kenya, east of Lake Victoria in Africa.

MATERIALISM the doctrine that only matter exists and that its properties can explain all phenomena of the Universe.

MEIOSIS process by which the chromosome number of a reproductive cell becomes reduced to half the diploid number.

MESSENGER RNA (MRNA) the molecule in which the genetic information encoded in the sequence of nucleotides of the deoxyribonucleic acid of the chromosomes in the nucleus is transcribed into a complementary sequence of nucleotides of ribonucleic acid.

MIGRATION movement of members of one population of organisms from one geographic area to another.

MITOCHONDRION organelle in the cytoplasm of plant and animal cells containing deoxyribonucleic acid and the enzymes needed for the storage of energy in the form of adenosime triphospate (ATP).

MITOSIS process by which the chromosomes of an organism after duplication are separated into daughter cells.

MONOGENISM the doctrine that all mankind descended from one original pair (Adam and Eve).

MONOPHYLETIC EVOLUTION (OF *HOMO SAPIENS*) the origin of *Homo sapiens* from one stem of progenitors.

MONOTHEISM belief in only one Supreme Being (God).

MORULA the stage in mammalian embryogenesis in which successive divisions of the zygote produce a solid ball of cells.

MTDNA mitochondrial DNA.

MUTATION a heritable change in a gene.

MYTH a story describing some event in the remote past.

NATURAL SELECTION a process in nature by which organisms better fitted to their environment leave more progeny with their characteristics to the next generation than organisms of the same species less well adapted.

NEURON a nerve cell

NEUTRON an electrically neutral particle forming part of the nucleus of an atom.

NUCLEIC ACID a linear molecule containing a sequence of many nucleotides.

NUCLEOTIDE a unit of a nucleic acid containing a phosphate, a pentose sugar, and an organic base.

ONTOGENY the embryonic development of an organism.

ORGANELLE a part of a cell carrying on a specialized function.

ORGANISM a living being whose parts are mutually interdependent and function for the benefit of the whole.

ORIGINAL SIN the sin committed by Adam and Eve in eating the fruit from the tree of the knowledge of good and evil contrary to the explicit prohibition of God.

ORTHOGENESIS evolution proceeding along a straight pathway.

OZONE a molecule of oxygen containing three oxygen atoms.

PARABLE a short fictitious narrative told to convey some religious truth.

PARADIGM a model explanation or pattern used to interpret natural phenomena.

PENTATEUCH the first five books of the Bible, viz. Genesis, Exodus, Leviticus, Numbers, Deuteronomy.

PEROXIDASE an enzyme hydrolyzing peroxides.

PHENOTYPE the observable characteristics of an organism.

PHILOGENY the evolutionary history of an organism.

PLACENTA a modified part of the chorion by which a mammalian fetus is nourished in the uterus of its mother.

POLYGENISM the opinion that mankind has descended from more than one pair of original humans.

POLYPEPTIDE a short compound consisting of two or more amino acids bonded together.

POLYPHILETIC EVOLUTION (OF *HOMO SAPIENS*) the origin of *Homo sapiens* from different stems.

POLYTHEISM belief in the existence of many gods.

PONGIDAE the Primate family containing the great apes (gorilla, chimpanzee, orangutan).

POSITIVISM the philosophical position that truth is limited to what can be observed by scientific methods.

PREADAPTATION the possession of traits needed for success in a new environment before actual experience of that environment.

PRIMATOLOGIST a professional student of the mammalian order Primates (monkeys, apes, humans).

PROCARYOTE an organism which lacks a nuclear membrane enclosing its chromosomes.

PROTEIN a molecule composed of a long series of amino acids bonded together in linear order.

PROTON a positively charged particle found in the nucleus of an atom.

PSILOPHYTE a primitive very simple vascular plant.

PURINE a nitrogenous organic compound with two closed rings.

PYRIMIDINE a nitrogenous organic compound with one closed ring.

RACE a subpopulation of a species whose members share certain characteristics distinctive of them.

RADIOACTIVE emitting ionizing radiation.

REDUCTIONISM the view that all properties of an organism can be explained by the chemistry and physics of its parts.

RESTRICTION ENZYME an enzyme that cuts both strands of DNA at a site specified by a short sequence of nucleotides.

REVELATION (DIVINE) God's disclosure of Himself or His will to mankind.

RIBONUCLEIC ACID (RNA) a nucleic acid in which the pentose sugar constituent is ribose.

RIBOSE a five carbon sugar molecule.

RIBOSOME cytoplasmic organelle on which proteins are synthesized.

SANCTIFYING GRACE a sharing in the life of God which empowers one to know God as He knows Himself and to love God as He loves Himself.

SAVANNA grassland with numerous trees scattered in it.

SCAVENGER one that lives on animal remains.

SCHOLASTIC PHILOSOPHER one whose logic, metaphysics, and so forth are grounded on the teachings of Aristotle as expounded chiefly by Thomas Aquinas.

SCIENTISM the view that truth can be attained only by the methods of natural science.

SELECTION (NATURAL) differential reproduction of organisms with different genotypes.

SOCIOBIOLOGY the scientific study of the biological bases for all forms of social behavior in all animals including humans.

SOUL (HUMAN) the immaterial principle responsible for a human's life and activities.

SPECIES a natural population of organisms whose members are fertile with each other but not with members of other populations.

SUBSTANCE as a technical term from Aristotelian philosophy, means a being which possesses its existence independently of its accidents.

THEORY an explanation of some natural phenomena supported by some scientific evidence.

THERMOLUMINESCENCE a method of dating flint from ancient fireplaces. The flints are gradually heated and the amount of light emitted is measured. The light represents the energy of electrons trapped inside when the flints were burnt. Since the rate of electron trapping is known, the measurement of the light emitted allows calculating the date of the original burning.

THYMINE a pyrimidine base found in deoxyribonucleic acid.

TRNA an RNA which carries amino acids to the ribosomes for assembly into proteins.

ULTRAVIOLET beyond the visible spectrum of light at the violet end.

ZYGOTE the cell produced by the union of male and female gametes.